A temperate Earth?

2

Photo on title page   The frozen landscape of eastern Greenland is so cold that a permanent ice-sheet is present, from which glaciers slowly spill out. Has the climate always been like this? And will it always remain so?

The Open University, Walton Hall, Milton Keynes MK7 6AA

First published 1998. Reprinted 2001, 2002

Written, edited, designed and typeset by the Open University.

Printed and bound in Singapore under the supervision of MRM Graphic Ltd, Winslow, Bucks.

ISBN 0 7492 8188 X

This text forms part of an Open University course, S103 *Discoveriong Science*. The complete list of texts that make up this course can be found on the back cover. Details of this and other Open University courses can be obtained from the Course Reservations and Sales Office, PO Box 724, The Open University, Milton Keynes MK7 6ZS, United Kingdom: tel. (00 44) 1908 653231.
For availability of this or other course components, contact Open University Worldwide Ltd, The Berrill Building, Walton Hall, Milton Keynes MK1 6AA, United Kingdom: tel. (00 44) 1908 858585,
fax (00 44) 1908 858787, e-mail ouwenq@open.ac.uk.
Alternatively, much useful course information can be obtained from the Open University's website
http://www.open.ac.uk

s103block2i1.4

Contents

Introduction

1

Imagine what would happen to life on Earth if outdoor temperatures rose or fell by a few degrees. This does not mean the day-to-day or season-by-season temperature changes with which we are all familiar. It means an overall change, a change in average temperature, in which year after year the temperature much of the time was either lower or higher than it had been in earlier decades.

Before you try to imagine the consequences, you need to be sure what is meant by 'a few degrees'. In this block the Celsius temperature scale is used, which was described in Box 4.1 of Block 1. On this scale, pure water in our everyday environment freezes at zero degrees Celsius (0 °C), and boils at one hundred degrees Celsius (100 °C). There are therefore 100 degrees Celsius between the normal freezing and boiling temperatures of water.

To reinforce your 'feel' for the Celsius scale, note that most of us would regard an outdoor temperature below about 5 °C as cold, and a temperature above about 30 °C as hot.

○ What is the difference between 30 °C and 5 °C?

○ The difference is 30 °C – 5 °C, which is 25 °C.

This 25 °C difference is much larger than the few degrees Celsius change in average temperature that we are considering here. A change of a few degrees Celsius therefore does not sound a lot, so you might conclude that the consequences for us would be slight. Closer inspection reveals a different picture, with significant effects on human life, and on life in general.

Question 1.1   Consider a region that experiences a change in average temperature of a few degrees Celsius. From your general knowledge, list one consequence in each of the following categories: the natural environment; agriculture; housing; transport.

You need not go into details. For example, in the natural environment 'changes in the types of tree' is all we would expect in your answer as one possibility.
[*Note*   Questions and activities are designed to help you learn via *active* study: please attempt them *before* looking at our answers and comments.] ◀

Consider first some of the regional consequences of a *rise* in average temperature of a few degrees Celsius. Roughly speaking, it turns out that the effects would be as if the region had been moved several hundred kilometres closer to the Equator. For example, central England would have a climate something like that of central France. Following such a rise in temperature, plants and animals adapted to warmer climates could spread to live nearer the poles. For example, in Europe the forests of birch that today are common in parts of Scotland and in Scandinavia could be replaced by the forests of ash, oak, hawthorn, beech, and the like now confined farther south. In addition, agriculture across the globe would face new challenges. For example, many cereals are so 'fine tuned' to climate that many cereal-growing areas would suffer a fall in productivity. On the other hand, certain crops could be grown in areas that are at present too cold to be very productive. Figure 1.1 shows the present northern limit for maize-growing in western Europe, a limit imposed in this region by insufficient warmth. You can see the considerable northern spread of this limit if average temperatures were to rise by a few degrees Celsius.

Figure 1.1 The present northern limit of maize-growing in western Europe, and the likely limit if average temperatures were to rise by a few degrees Celsius.

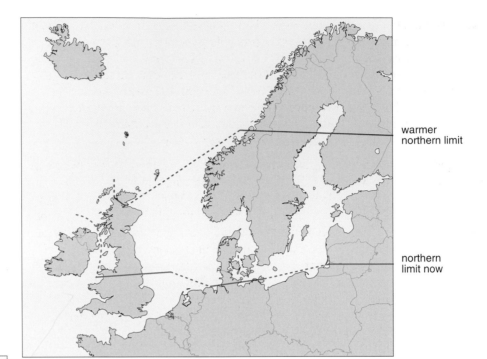

warmer
northern limit

northern
limit now

Figure 1.2 Areas of mainland Britain that are presently less than 5 m above sea-level.

A further effect of a rise in average temperature of a few degrees Celsius would be a rise in sea-level. There are two contributions to this rise. First, ocean water increases in volume when its temperature rises; this is a general phenomenon observed in all solids, liquids and gases over almost all ranges of temperature, and is called thermal expansion. Second, liquid water would be liberated from ice, largely as a result of the partial melting of mountain glaciers and of the Greenland ice-sheet.

Although the exact value is uncertain, a 30 cm rise in sea-level is a possible consequence of a 3 °C rise in average temperature across the whole surface of the Earth. This might not sound much, but it would threaten large areas of Bangladesh, the southern USA, and southern China — areas that are densely populated. Figure 1.2 shows the areas of mainland Britain that are less than 5 m above the present average sea-level. A 30 cm or so sea-level rise would threaten these areas more than any others in the region. This does not mean that a part of the country in which you might have a particular interest would disappear beneath the waves, but that it would be more susceptible to sea-flooding at high tide and high wind. We wouldn't have to despair and accept this: barriers could be built to keep the sea at bay, as many inhabitants of the Netherlands will testify.

Another effect of a rise in temperature is that, in regions that are currently cool, less fuel would be needed for heating dwellings and workplaces in winter, though there might be a greater need for summer air conditioning. Some cities could sell off their snow ploughs.

These are just a few of the possible consequences of a rise in average temperature of a few degrees Celsius. Let's now consider, briefly, some consequences of a *fall* in average temperature by a few degrees Celsius.

○ List a few possible consequences of such a fall.

○ Our selection is in the following paragraph, but please try to write down a few consequences of your own *before* reading on. Reversing some of the consequences of a rise in temperature is a good approach.

Sea-level would fall, but not enough to put the English Channel ferry operators out of business. Existing mountain glaciers would probably get larger, and glaciers could appear in new places, such as in the highlands of the UK. Northern seas could freeze more often, and parts of Scandinavia could become covered in an ice-sheet. In Europe there would be a tendency for northern birch forest to spread south. Dwellings and workplaces would have to be better insulated to avoid huge heating bills, though the need for air conditioning in southern Europe would be reduced. There would be comparable consequences elsewhere on Earth.

Clearly, modest temperature changes would alter our lives, and the lives of the plants and animals with which we share this planet. Moreover, temperature is just *one* aspect of climate. Others include wind and precipitation. Many of the effects outlined above depend in part on changes in these other aspects, notably in precipitation. For example, crops need rain as well as warmth, and in Block 1 you saw how important water is for all life on this planet. Climate change in all its aspects is therefore a subject of enormous current interest, as reflected by international conferences, and international agreements on limiting human activities that might already be a cause of climate change. However, of all the different aspects of climate, temperature is particularly important, both in itself, and because changes in many of the other aspects of climate result from a change in temperature.

Notice that we are referring to climate rather than weather. There is an important distinction between these two terms. 'Weather' refers to the day-to-day meteorological conditions at a particular place, whereas 'climate' refers to the long-term prevalent weather conditions. A change in the weather is short-lived and something we can usually cope with, even in extreme cases of heavy snow, flooding or high summer temperatures. A change in climate, however, in which rainfall or temperature is significantly different in the long term, can have more serious consequences.

The temperature aspect of climate is so important that it has been made the main subject of this block. You will see that in order to explore it we shall draw on a wide variety of traditional scientific subjects, notably Earth sciences (which includes geology and atmospheric science), physics, astronomy, chemistry, and biology. These subjects are not themselves of central interest in this block; instead, we draw on them as needed for the story. In this respect Block 2 differs from most of the later blocks in *Discovering Science*, in that its main aim is to explore how science can be used to understand a particular issue. The science that we have included in Block 2 to support the story is basic, but important, and will be built on in later blocks.

1.1 Outline of Block 2

Sections 2 and 3 present some of the evidence that indicates that average temperatures (near the Earth's surface) were different in the past. We go back to well before there were any written records, and so we describe means of estimating temperatures in the distant past that do not involve the use of a manufactured thermometer — we have to rely on natural 'thermometers'. Having demonstrated that temperatures have changed significantly throughout the past, we then investigate the causes. This investigation constitutes Sections 4–9, and thus takes up most of the block.

Sections 4 and 5 outline the factors that determine the average surface temperature over the whole planet. This gives a broad view, an overall picture, from which we have chosen to concentrate on the role of the Earth's atmosphere in determining the global average temperature. Section 6 describes the atmosphere as a whole, and then homes in on two important atmospheric gases, water vapour and carbon dioxide. Their effect on temperature depends on how much of each of them there is in the atmosphere. We must therefore consider the extent to which the amounts of water vapour and carbon dioxide in the atmosphere are fixed. Section 7 addresses this question for water, and Section 8 for carbon dioxide. These sections show how these two gases are tied in with global cycles that involve not only the atmosphere, but also the oceans, the Earth's interior, the Earth's surface, and the plants and animals that live on the surface. In Section 8 there is a CD-ROM activity intended to reinforce your understanding of the global carbon cycle.

Section 9 returns to the broad picture, and centres on our present ability to understand the reasons for past temperature changes. This section includes a CD-ROM activity in which you can investigate not only the effect on the global average temperature of varying the amounts of atmospheric carbon dioxide and water vapour, but also the effects of some of the other factors that you will have met in Section 5. For each factor that you vary, climate models on the CD-ROM calculate a new global average temperature and also how the temperature changes in different regions. A crucial test is whether climate models can account for past temperature changes, and Section 9 reveals whether they can. If they can, then we have some confidence that they can predict the future.

Section 10 takes us into the future, particularly by discussing the predictions of temperature change over the next several decades, and the role of human activities in determining the size and speed of the changes. An increase in the amount of carbon dioxide in the atmosphere is a particularly important consequence of human activity, and so a major feature of Section 10 is that it builds on the story of carbon dioxide in Section 8.

This introduction to Block 2 has set the scene for what is to follow. You might find it useful to refer to it later if you want to remind yourself of the overall storyline of the block, particularly when you return to your study of this block after a break of more than a day or so.

Woven into the story is further development of important skills that are used by scientists. You will have the opportunity to practise skills that you have been developing in Block 1, notably: organizing your study time; reading the text 'actively'; writing short descriptions or explanations; developing and revising maths skills. You will also be able to extend your skills, in particular: writing longer pieces than you did in Block 1; acquiring some further maths skills; handling scientific information in the form of tables, diagrams and graphs; thinking about how to make your learning more effective. You will carry out some practical work, which will help you to develop skills such as designing apparatus, making measurements and deciding how reliable they are. You will develop your ability to use models and analogies to help visualize and understand abstract and difficult concepts. Finally, in addition to the course components that you met in Block 1, you will be learning for the first time from interactive materials presented on CD-ROM, and there are important study skills to be acquired here too, to get the most out of them.

Activity 1.1 Planning your study of Block 2

Before you start on Section 2, you should take a few minutes to plan carefully your study time over the four weeks that are allocated for the study of Block 2. At the end of Section 5 you will be asked to review progress, and you will be given advice about how to revise your study plans, should this be necessary. ◀

As with Block 1, you will find additional notes on each activity in the Study File. You should always consult these notes before starting an activity as they will often provide further detail on what to do or guidance on how to approach a particular activity.

2 The Earth's surface temperatures today and in the recent past

To speculate on the consequences of a change in the Earth's climate is one thing; to decide whether it *is* changing requires observational evidence. In the context of this block, the crucial evidence comes from measurements of surface temperature, both in the present and in the past. Our quest to understand the Earth's surface temperature starts by recognizing the importance of making careful measurements.

2.1 The Earth's surface temperature

In this section, we shall be concerned with making observations of the Earth's surface temperature, in particular the air temperature near the ground. Later sections will be concerned with the way scientists seek to explain the observations. To reach the correct explanations, it is important that the observations — the starting point of the process — are carefully made. To begin with, we need to specify what we mean by the Earth's surface air temperature. In science, this comes down to a specification of how we measure it. 'Just stick a thermometer in the air' is not an adequate specification. One reason is that the temperature near the ground varies with height, and therefore a few centimetres above the ground it can be several degrees different from what it is, say, a metre above the ground.

○ Can you think of another reason for a better specification?

○ Another important reason is the effect of direct sunlight on the temperature indicated by most thermometers: just recall how much hotter you feel in the sunshine than in the shade.

The full specification of how to measure temperature will not concern us, but the essence is to place a thermometer in a well-ventilated white box in an open space about a metre above the ground; this box is called a Stevenson screen (Figure 2.1). Every day at a set time, the temperature of the air is recorded. This temperature is then regarded as the **Earth's surface temperature** at that location, at the time of measurement. Measurements of the water and air temperatures at sea are also routinely taken.

Figure 2.1   A Stevenson screen, open to show thermometers (mounted centrally) and other meteorological instruments.

If we were to take temperature readings twice a day, say, for a year we would end up with a large number of measurements. How can we reduce these to just one temperature value, which would be representative of the year? The answer to this question requires the concept of an average, or mean, temperature.

2.1.1 Mean surface temperature

The idea of 'averaging' is to be able to give a single figure that best represents a fluctuating quantity, like temperature at a given location. In everyday speech the word 'average' can be used to describe any typical or characteristic attribute of something. However, this is a rather loose definition and can sometimes lead to confusion over exactly what is meant. To overcome this problem, scientists define the term **mean** as the sum of a series of measurements divided by the number of those measurements.

To take an actual example, Table 2.1 reports the twenty-four hourly surface temperature readings from 00.00 (midnight) to 23.00 (11 p.m.) taken on 14 July 1996 in Milton Keynes. Rather than poring over the numbers in the table, the easiest way to get a picture of how the temperature varied throughout the day is to plot, on a graph, each temperature reading against the time it was taken, as in Figure 2.2. Before looking at the information on this graph, you should note how the axes are labelled. The horizontal axis is the time during the day in hours, starting at zero hours (midnight) and using the 24-hour clock.

○ Where does the vertical (temperature) axis start, and why doesn't it start at 0 °C?

○ It starts at 14 °C. If it had started at 0 °C, then we would have had a large vacant space in the bottom half of the graph, with the plotted information occupying just the top half of the diagram. As well as being a waste of space this would have made it more difficult to read the plotted information accurately, so the scales and ranges of the axes on a graph are chosen to make the best use of the space on the page.

Table 2.1 The temperature in Milton Keynes every hour from 00.00 (midnight) to 23.00 (11 p.m.) on 14 July 1996. These data are plotted in Figure 2.2.

Time/hours	Temperature/°C	Time/hours	Temperature/°C
00.00	16.4	12.00	19.2
01.00	15.9	13.00	20.1
02.00	15.3	14.00	20.3
03.00	15.0	15.00	21.6
04.00	16.0	16.00	23.1
05.00	15.7	17.00	24.5
06.00	15.8	18.00	25.2
07.00	16.0	19.00	24.8
08.00	17.0	20.00	23.7
09.00	17.4	21.00	21.9
10.00	17.4	22.00	18.9
11.00	18.1	23.00	16.5

Figure 2.2 Graph showing how the surface temperature at Milton Keynes varied over a 24-hour period, 14 July 1996. Each dot represents one temperature reading. The curved line drawn through the points shows the overall trend more clearly and allows temperatures at times between measurements to be estimated.

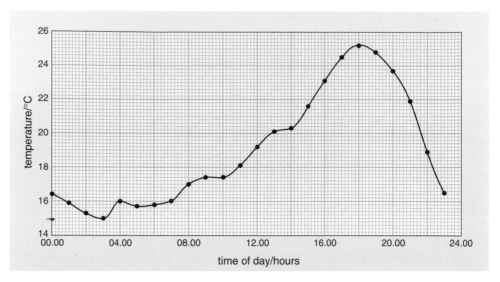

The graph immediately shows the daily cycle of warming and cooling. The peak in the graph allows us quickly to spot when the maximum temperature occurred. And likewise, the lowest temperature and its time are also easier to spot by glancing at the graph than by scanning down the columns of numbers in Table 2.1.

Question 2.1   What are the maximum and minimum temperatures in the 24-hour period plotted in Figure 2.2, and at what times do they occur? ◄

To summarize these two extreme measurements, we can work out their mean. From the definition of a mean, stated in the first paragraph of this section, we get the following word equation (note that it has been given a number so that we can refer to it later; we shall follow this practice throughout the course):

the mean *equals* the sum of the measurements *divided by* the number of measurements   (2.1)

Therefore the mean of the two extreme temperatures equals

$$\frac{(25.2\ °C + 15.0\ °C)}{2} = \frac{(40.2\ °C)}{2} = 20.1\ °C$$

What is the mean of *all* the temperature measurements in Figure 2.2? Again, it is the sum of measurements divided by the number of measurements; this is the **mean surface temperature**. This is best calculated by reading the measured values from the table rather than trying to read the values from the graph.

● The first step in calculating the mean temperature is to add all the temperature values in Table 2.1 together. What value do you get?

○ 455.8 °C.

● The second step is to count the number of measurements. How many are there?

○ 24.

● The third and final step is to divide the total of the surface temperature measurements by the number of measurements: $\frac{455.8\ °C}{24}$. What is the value of the mean?

○ If you do this sum on your calculator, you will probably get a result displayed as 18.99166..., where the string of dots indicates that the series of digits is longer than we have given.

The answer of 18.991 66... °C contains many decimal places (the .991 66... part), but not all of these digits can be significant, given that the original temperature readings are recorded to only one decimal place. We cannot be certain about the digit that represents thousandths of a degree, let alone the digit that represents millionths of a degree. Scientists have conventions for the number of digits that they quote in the answer to a calculation like this, and these are discussed in Box 2.1, *Uncertainties and significant figures*, which we recommend that you study now. In the present case, the uncertainty in taking a reading from the thermometer is about ± 0.1 °C, so we quote the temperatures and the mean temperature to one decimal place, which in this case corresponds to three significant figures. Applying the rules for rounding numbers introduced in Block 1 (Box 3.2), 18.991 66... °C is rounded up to 19.0 °C. The mean surface temperature at Milton Keynes on 14 July 1996, then, was 19.0 °C.

Box 2.1   *Uncertainties and significant figures*

The temperature measurements in Table 2.1 are all recorded to one decimal place. But what determines the number of digits that we record when we make a measurement like this? Why, for example, is the first temperature recorded as 16.4 °C, rather than 16 °C, or 16.42 °C?

Figure 2.3 shows two thermometers that are measuring the same air temperature. Thermometer A is indicating that the temperature is between 16 °C and 17 °C, so it is 'sixteen point something' °C. The 'something' cannot be read precisely — but it is a bit less than half-way between the divisions corresponding to 16 °C and 17 °C, so we might record the temperature as 16.4 °C. We cannot be very confident about the value of this last digit; some people might record the temperature as 16.3 °C and others as 16.5 °C, rather than 16.4 °C. Even the same person reading this thermometer might sometimes record the temperature as 16.4 °C, sometimes 16.5 °C, sometimes 16.3 °C. Because we are uncertain about the digit in the first decimal place, there is clearly no point in trying to 'guess' a second decimal place here.

Now have a look at thermometer B in Figure 2.3, which has scale divisions every 0.1 °C.

● What temperature is indicated by thermometer B?

○ The temperature is between 16.4 °C and 16.5 °C. The second decimal place is rather uncertain, but it appears to be about 7, so we would record the temperature as 16.47 °C. However, you might have thought that the last digit should be 6 or 8, or possibly even 5 or 9.

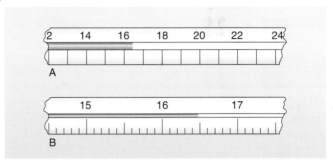

Figure 2.3   Two thermometers, A and B, with different scale divisions. Both are measuring the air temperature in the same place.

We can indicate how well we know the value of a measured quantity by quoting explicitly the uncertainty in that value. For the temperature measured by thermometer A, we estimated that the possible range was between 16.3 °C and 16.5 °C. This means that we are fairly confident that the temperature is within 0.1 °C of 16.4 °C. The temperature could be as low as (16.4 − 0.1) °C or as high as (16.4 + 0.1) °C. This would be quoted as (16.4 ± 0.1) °C, and we would speak this as 'sixteen point four plus or minus zero point one degrees Celsius'. The temperature measured by thermometer B would be quoted as (16.47 ± 0.02) °C. The ± quantity (± 0.1 °C in the first case and ± 0.02 °C in the second) is usually referred to as the **uncertainty** in the measurement. We would say that the first measurement of 16.4 °C has an uncertainty associated with it of ± 0.1 °C, and the second measurement of 16.47 °C has an uncertainty of ± 0.02 °C.

13

The thermometers in Figure 2.3 have illustrated the fact that there are uncertainties associated with reading a measuring instrument. But there are other types of uncertainty in measurements that we may need to consider too. Perhaps the air temperature fluctuates on a fairly short time-scale owing to variations in the wind and cloud cover, so that a series of measurements over a couple of minutes shows a range of values. In this case too we could quantify the uncertainty by quoting the range of values. This type of uncertainty and the uncertainties in reading values from a scale are examples of **random uncertainties**, so called because the measured values are scattered fairly randomly about some mean value. We can get an estimate of the combined effect of all of the random uncertainties associated with a measurement by repeating it a number of times: the spread of the results is an indication of the random uncertainties that are present.

Measurements that have a small random uncertainty are said to be precise, or to be of high **precision**. Another way of expressing this is to say that if we reduce the random uncertainty in a measurement (for example, by using a better measuring instrument), then we make the measurement more precise, or in other words we increase the precision of the measurement. Thus the temperature measured by thermometer B (Figure 2.3) has a smaller random uncertainty and it is more precise (it has a greater precision) than the temperature measured by thermometer A.

There is yet another type of uncertainty in measurements that is rather more difficult to assess. We'll illustrate this with the thermometer example again. The scale might be incorrectly located on the thermometer, so that, for example, the temperature recorded is always 0.5 °C higher than the actual value. This causes what is known as a systematic error, or **systematic uncertainty**, in the temperatures that are recorded — they are all 0.5 °C too high. Or suppose that the Stevenson screen is incorrectly constructed; perhaps it is painted the wrong colour, so that it absorbs too much solar radiation, or it has too much ventilation, or it is at the wrong height from the ground. All of these could lead to systematic differences between the measured temperature and the temperature that would have been measured if the approved screen design had been used. Again these 'problems' cause systematic uncertainties in the temperatures that are recorded. Measurements that have small systematic uncertainties are said to be **accurate**. So describing a measurement as accurate is not the same as describing it as precise.

The difference between random and systematic uncertainties is illustrated in Figure 2.4. Random uncertainties lead to a random distribution of the measured values around a 'true' value, and large and small random uncertainties are shown in parts (a) and (b) of the figure. A systematic uncertainty leads to an offset of the measured values from the 'true' value, as shown in Figure 2.4c.

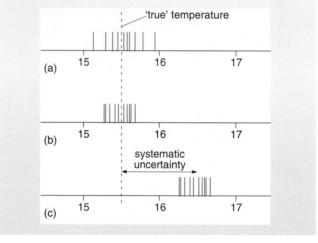

Figure 2.4 Measured values of temperature are indicated by the positions of the vertical lines on the temperature scales. (a) Large random uncertainties mean that measurements are randomly scattered in a large range about the 'true' value. (b) Smaller random uncertainties lead to a smaller spread, but still clustered around the 'true' value. (c) A systematic uncertainty combined with a small random uncertainty leads to the measurements all being displaced from the 'true' value.

Significant figures

When quoting a value for a measured quantity, you should never give more digits than you can justify in terms of the uncertainties in the measurements. The smaller the uncertainties in the measurements, the greater will be the number of digits that can be quoted. The number of digits that you quote when you write down the value of a quantity is known as the number of **significant figures**. We would say that a value of 16.4 °C is quoted to three significant figures, and this is commonly abbreviated to three sig figs, whereas the value 16.47 °C is quoted to four significant figures. In general, the last significant figure will be somewhat uncertain, but you will be confident about the other figures. Thus the temperature indicated by thermometer A in Figure 2.3

might actually have been 16.3 °C or 16.5 °C, so the final digit is uncertain, but we are confident about the 16 °C part.

○ How many significant figures are quoted in the following values: 1 345 °C, 13.45 °C, 1.345 °C and 1.3 °C?

○ The first three temperatures are quoted to four significant figures, but there are only two significant figures in 1.3 °C.

Specifying the number of significant figures when zeros are involved can be a bit more tricky, as the following examples indicate.

• 0.082 m: here there are only two significant figures because *initial zeros do not count*. These initial zeros tell you only about the size of the number, and not about the precision to which it is known. The first significant figure in this value is the 8.

• 50.6 m: there are three significant figures here, since the zero in the middle of a number counts as a significant figure in the same way as the other digits.

• 79.0 m: there are three significant figures here too; a zero that is at the end of a number and is after the decimal point has the same significance as any other digit; if this value was known to only two significant figures then it would have been quoted as 79 m.

• 900 m: this is the really tricky one! It could be that the value is known to three significant figures, that is, only the final zero is uncertain. But it might be that the distance has been measured only to the nearest 100 m (i.e. it lies between 850 m and 950 m). One way around this ambiguity is to state clearly the number of figures that are significant; for example, to quote '900 m to two sig figs'. Another option is to quote the uncertainty explicitly, for example, 900 m ± 20 m, or 900 m ± 5 m. Alternatively, we can use scientific notation to resolve the ambiguity. Thus 9.00×10^2 m, 9.0×10^2 m and 9×10^2 m are all 900 m, but expressed to three sig figs, two sig figs and one sig fig, respectively.

○ To how many significant figures are each of the following measurements given: (a) 1.240 mm (b) 0.019 mm (c) 10.009 5 mm?

○ (a) Four sig figs. (b) Two sig figs. (c) Six sig figs.

In Block 1 you met another way of specifying the number of digits in a value, namely the *number of decimal places*, and this is the number of digits following the decimal point. Thus the three numbers in the question you have just answered are quoted to three, three, and four decimal places, respectively. However, quoting numbers of decimal places is not very helpful when dealing with large or small numbers that involve powers of ten, and as you will see shortly, it is much more helpful to think in terms of significant figures when multiplying and dividing numbers.

Of course, the results of measurements are often used in calculations, and we then need to know how many figures to quote in the answer. You will be well aware that multiplying and dividing numbers with your calculator can lead to a long string of digits. For example, if you measured the air temperature at midday on three successive days as 14.5 °C, 14.1 °C and 14.4 °C, then the mean temperature would be

$$\frac{14.5 \,°C + 14.1 \,°C + 14.4 \,°C}{3} = \frac{43.0 \,°C}{3} = 14.333 \,°C$$

according to a calculator that displayed five digits. It is not sensible to quote all of these digits in the answer because they imply a precision to the measurements that is not justified. But how should the answer be quoted — 14 °C, 14.3 °C, 14.33 °C, or what?

There are two basic 'rules-of-thumb' that we use to determine the number of digits that we quote in an answer. Both procedures act only as rough guides. They are:

When multiplying and dividing numbers, the number of *significant figures* in the result should be the same as in the measurement with the fewest significant figures. For example, if the length of a flower bed is measured as 4.5 m and its width as 1.09 m, then the calculated area is 4.5 m × 1.09 m = 4.905 m². However, since the length of 4.5 m is measured to only two significant figures, we are only justified in quoting the area to two significant figures, so we would round the calculated value to 4.9 m² (see Block 1, Box 3.2).

When adding and subtracting numbers, you have to think in terms of *decimal places* rather than in terms of significant figures. The number of decimal places in the result should be the same as in the measurement with the least number of decimal places; note that this rule assumes that there *are* decimal places and that either the numbers are not written in powers of ten notation, or the numbers all involve the same power of ten. For example, if the mass of a bag of potatoes was measured as 12.8 kg, and we added to it a potato with a mass of 0.33 kg, then the calculated value of the total mass would be 13.13 kg. However, since the first mass was measured to only one decimal place, we are only justified in quoting the total mass to one decimal place, so we would round the calculated value to 13.1 kg, which happens to be three significant figures. (Note that this rule really applies when you are dealing only with a few numbers; if you are adding many numbers, then the combination of the uncertainties in each of the individual numbers will produce a larger uncertainty in the total, and thus reduce the number of decimal places that is quoted.)

Question 2.2 Do the following calculations and express your answers to the appropriate number of significant figures: (a) 0.43 m + 1.217 m; (b) 8.1 kg − 3.82 kg; (c) 2.373 m × 3.6 m; (d) 6 342 kg ÷ 2.42 m³. ◄

You need to be careful when applying these rules-of-thumb to calculations involving whole numbers. For example, if the mass of an object is 2.17 g, then the mass of five of these objects is 5 × 2.17 g = 10.85 g. How many significant figures should we use for the answer? You might think that only one significant figure should be used, since the number 5 was only expressed to one significant figure. However, there is no uncertainty in this value; when we say five objects we mean *exactly* five objects, and so this number is known very precisely. The limiting precision here is in the mass of 2.17 g, which is quoted to three significant figures, and so the answer must be rounded to three significant figures, that is 10.9 g.

Let us return to the question about how to quote the mean value of the three temperatures 14.5 °C, 14.1 °C and 14.4 °C. The sum of these values is 43.0 °C, and this is quoted to one decimal place, because this is the number of decimal places in the individual measurements. The mean is $\frac{43.0\ °C}{3}$, and this is quoted as 14.3 °C, where there are three significant figures in the answer because there are three significant figures in the value 43.0 from which it was calculated.

We introduced the idea of significant figures in the context of measurements so that the link with the precision, accuracy and uncertainties in measurements could be emphasized. Almost all of the numbers that we quote in this course will be measured values of some quantity or another, and the number of significant figures quoted will be an indication of the uncertainty in the value. When doing calculations with these values, you will need to bear in mind the rules-of-thumb outlined above for deciding how many significant figures should be quoted in the answer.

Just as we calculated a daily mean temperature, it is possible to calculate an **annual mean surface temperature** using measurements taken at frequent and regular intervals throughout a year. The procedure for calculating the annual mean surface temperature can be written down as:

$$\text{annual mean surface temperature} = \frac{\text{sum of all temperature values}}{\text{number of temperature values}} \qquad (2.2)$$

Question 2.3 In 1995, the temperature at a location in central England was measured at 06.00 hours and 18.00 hours every day. The sum of these temperatures is 6 647 °C.

(a) Calculate the annual mean surface temperature at this location, expressing your answer to two significant figures.

(b) Apart from using a more accurate thermometer, how would you improve the measurement procedure to obtain a more accurate annual mean surface temperature for the location in future? ◄

Of course, no two years are identical, either because an unusually cold or unusually warm year comes along every now and then, or because of longer term warming or cooling. To avoid the vagaries of an unusual year, and to serve as a benchmark against which to judge annual mean temperatures, meteorologists have adopted a convention of calculating a 30-year mean surface temperature. As its name implies, the **30-year mean surface temperature** is arrived at in the following way.

1   The surface temperature is recorded several times a day, every day for a period of 30 years.

2   The 30-year mean surface temperature is then calculated by adding up all the temperature values, and dividing the sum by the total number of values.

For example, suppose that at a certain location, the temperature has been measured 10 times a day for 30 years from 1961 to 1990 inclusive. Not forgetting the seven leap years, the number of days is

$(365 \times 30$ days$) + 7$ days $= 10\,957$ days

and hence the number of measurements is

$10\,957 \times 10 = 109\,570$ measurements

Suppose also that the sum of the 109 570 temperature readings is $8.861\,3 \times 10^5$ °C. Therefore, the 30-year mean surface temperature at that location is $8.861\,3 \times 10^5$ °C divided by 109 570, which is 8.087 3 °C. Note that we have quoted the sum of the temperatures to five significant figures. However, quoting this number of significant figures for the mean temperature is not justified because uncertainties in taking readings from the thermometer used may well be about ± 0.1 °C. There will therefore be some uncertainty in the first decimal place, so we will quote the mean temperature as 8.1 °C.

By calculating a mean surface temperature, we smooth out the variability of the weather at any particular location. For example, the 30-year mean surface temperature in Birmingham is 9.6 °C, but the highest recorded temperature there is a very hot 33 °C, and the lowest is a frigid –12 °C. However, our quest in this block is to understand what determines the *mean* temperature, and not the short-term variations above and below it. Moreover, we are interested in the Earth as a whole — we want the global picture.

2.1.2   Global mean surface temperature

Our primary concern is with the mean surface temperature averaged over the whole surface of the Earth, both land and sea — the **global mean surface temperature (GMST)**. Usually the average is over one or more years. Thus, to obtain the GMST, we have to obtain the mean surface temperature at a very large number of locations across the globe, and work out *their* mean value, as follows:

$$\text{GMST} = \frac{\text{sum of all mean surface temperatures}}{\text{number of surface locations}} \tag{2.3}$$

This is illustrated for a more restricted region in Question 2.4.

Question 2.4   (a) Calculate the UK 30-year mean surface temperature, from the data given in Figure 2.5. Give your answer to two significant figures.

(b) What would need to be done to obtain a more representative value? ◀

The value for the UK 30-year mean surface temperature given by the data in Figure 2.5 is not as good as it could be. This is because the locations do not give an even coverage of the UK: there are too many in the south, and too many at the coast. A more representative value is 9.2 °C, obtained from 25 weather stations distributed more evenly across the country. For calculating the GMST, it is desirable to spread thermometers uniformly over the globe. In practice, however, the spread is not

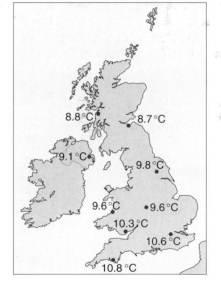

Figure 2.5   The 30-year mean surface temperature at a few locations in the UK.

uniform, with weather stations being few and far between in remote cold polar regions and over the oceans. To avoid the GMST being biased towards values from densely-monitored areas, a mean temperature is calculated for each region of the Earth and these mean values are combined into a single GMST. Whatever the method, finding the GMST involves a huge international effort requiring literally millions of measurements, all carefully done, documented and assessed for accuracy.

If the GMST corresponds to 30 consecutive years of averaging then it is called the 30-year GMST. Table 2.2 summarizes our naming convention for all these different mean temperatures. For the period 1961 to 1990, the 30-year GMST is 15 °C. But given our concerns about possible changes in the GMST, we will need to look at the history of variation in annual GMST values.

Table 2.2 The naming convention for the various mean temperatures.

Name	Meaning
mean surface temperature	the surface temperature at some location or over some region, averaged over some (unspecified) time-span
annual mean surface temperature	the surface temperature at some location or over some region, averaged over a year
30-year mean surface temperature	the surface temperature at some location or over some region, averaged over 30 consecutive years
global mean surface temperature (GMST)	the mean surface temperature averaged over the whole globe, usually over one or more years
30-year global mean surface temperature (30-year GMST)	the mean surface temperature averaged over the whole globe, over 30 consecutive years

Activity 2.1   Measuring precipitation

You should now break off from studying the book in order to start some practical work in which you will set up a simple rain gauge and use it to record precipitation throughout the four weeks allocated to the study of Block 2. This will not only help you to develop practical science skills but also help you to understand the idea of a mean value. It will require only about one hour of your time in total, but spread over the next four weeks. Therefore you should start this practical work as soon as possible. ◀

2.2   Temperatures in the recent past

To assess whether the annual mean surface temperature has changed or remained constant, our first step is to obtain accurate measurements. We would like to have a series of temperature readings extending as far back in time as possible to compare with present-day temperatures. The earliest temperature measurements were made in 1597 when the Italian scientist Galileo Galilei invented a thermometer. However, the particular instrument he invented was unreliable. It was not until 1632 that a French doctor, Jean Rey, invented the familiar type of liquid-filled thermometer described in Box 2.2, *How does a thermometer work*?

Having invented a thermometer, the next step was to devise a scale of measurement
— nobody had previously needed to quantify how cold or hot things were. At least 77
different scales are known to have been thought up, each defining two reference
temperatures and dividing the intervening temperature range into a number of equal
steps. Most were impractical, however, because they used reference temperatures that
were not fixed, like the temperature of blood and the melting temperature of butter.
The Celsius scale, defined by the normal freezing and boiling temperatures of pure
water (Block 1, Box 4.1), was proposed in 1743, though it wasn't named in honour of
its inventor until 1948.

Box 2.2   *How does a thermometer work?*

Figure 2.6 shows a typical liquid-filled thermometer.
You have probably used one at some time in the past,
but how does it work? Why is the scale marked off in
evenly spaced divisions?

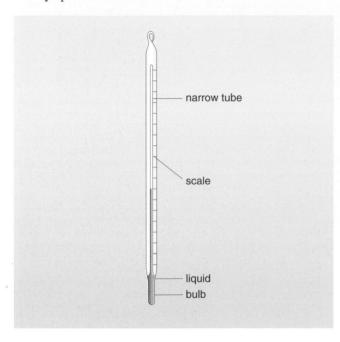

Figure 2.6   A liquid-filled thermometer.

The basis of a liquid-filled thermometer is the fact that
virtually all substances expand when they are heated and
contract when they cool down (just like the oceans in
Section 1). The amount of expansion depends on two
things: the size of the temperature increase, and the
substance used. Measuring the amount of expansion (or
contraction) for a given substance will therefore tell us
the size of the temperature change.

The most convenient type of substance to use is a liquid.
Water can be used but will not work at temperatures
below its freezing temperature. To overcome this
problem mercury can be used (it freezes at −39 °C), but
in the very cold climates of Siberia and northwestern
Canada this too is useless, so alcohol-filled
thermometers are used — ordinary alcohol (as found in
alcoholic drinks) freezes at −117 °C.

To observe the amount of expansion or contraction, the
liquid is held in a narrow transparent tube with a bulb at
the base. When the bulb is heated, the volume of liquid
in the bulb increases and the excess liquid volume has to
pass into the narrow tube. Because the tube is so narrow,
a small change in liquid volume becomes a large change
in the length of the liquid in the tube. When the bulb is
cooled the opposite happens, liquid in the tube retreating
into the bulb.

The larger the temperature change, the larger is the
change in length of the liquid. In fact, the connection
between the changes in temperature and length of liquid
is very regular. For instance, an increase of 2 °C will
cause an increase in length that is twice that caused by a
1 °C increase; an increase of 10 °C will cause an
expansion that is ten times that of a 1 °C increase, and so
on. This is why the scale marks on a thermometer are
evenly spaced. We say that the change in length is
proportional to the change in temperature. For every
1 °C increase in temperature, water expands in volume
by about 0.021%, mercury by about 0.018%, and alcohol
by about 0.11%.

In Britain, daily temperature measurements appear to have been made first in 1664 by
Robert Hooke, an experimental scientist better known for his discoveries in physics,
chemistry and biology. Other people started to maintain similar records, but
unfortunately each sequence of readings did not continue for very long. Moreover,
many observers in the 18th century would record the temperature in an unheated

north-facing room, but exactly how this relates to the outdoor temperature is uncertain. The longest continuous record from one place that extends to the present day is from the Radcliffe Observatory in Oxford, started in 1815. But even this impressive collection of data (Figure 2.7) is not ideal because the procedures for taking the measurements changed at various times, introducing the possibility that not all the measurements are strictly comparable.

So, although temperature measurements have been made for several hundred years, making sense of the surviving records is by no means straightforward. The problems are related to questions of experimental design, similar to those you are meeting in Activity 2.1 in relation to the design of an effective rain gauge. For temperature measurements, these problems are overcome today by the convention of using a Stevenson screen (Figure 2.1) positioned in open space away from shade to provide a standard and reliable method of measurement.

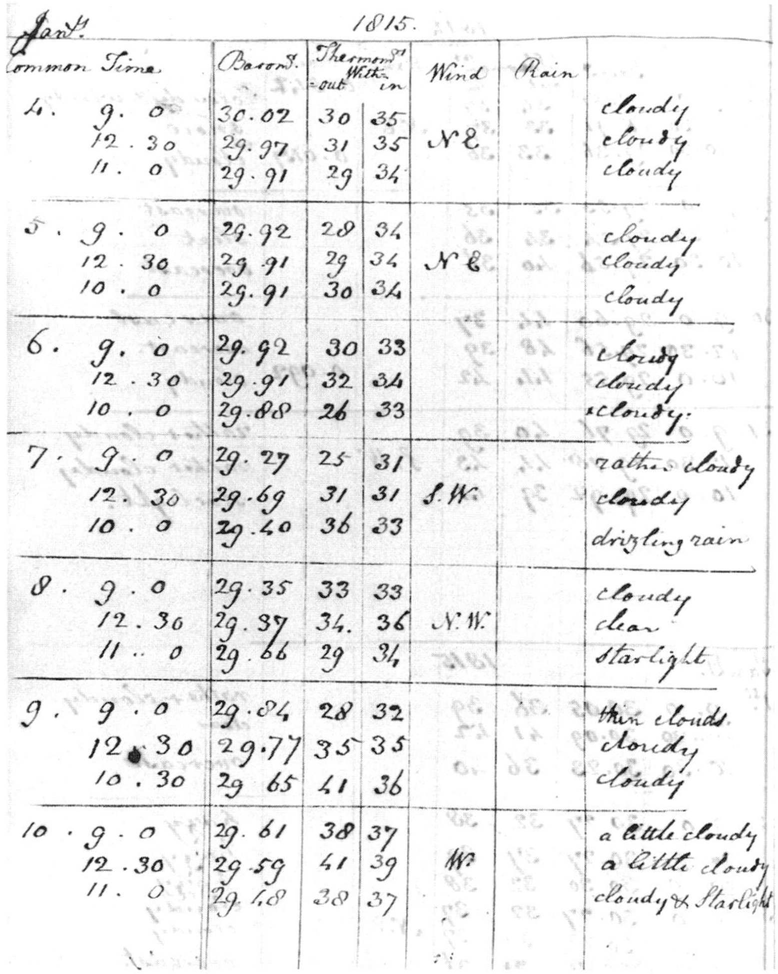

Jany. 1815.

Common Time		Baromr.	Thermomr With-out	Thermomr With-in	Wind	Rain	
4.	9 . 0	30.02	30	35			cloudy
	12 . 30	29.97	31	35	N E		cloudy
	11 . 0	29.91	29	34			cloudy
5.	9 . 0	29.92	28	34			cloudy
	12 . 30	29.91	29	34	N E		cloudy
	10 . 0	29.91	30	34			cloudy
6.	9 . 0	29.92	30	33			cloudy
	12 . 30	29.91	32	34			cloudy
	10 . 0	29.88	26	33			cloudy
7.	9 . 0	29.77	25	31			rather cloudy
	12 . 30	29.69	31	31	S.W.		cloudy
	10 . 0	29.40	36	33			drizzling rain
8.	9 . 0	29.35	33	33			cloudy
	12 . 30	29.37	34.	36	N.W.		clear
	11 . 0	29.66	29	34			starlight
9.	9 . 0	29.84	28	32			thin clouds
	12 . 30	29.77	35	35			cloudy
	10 . 30	29 65	41	36			cloudy
10	9 . 0	29.61	38	37			a little cloudy
	12 . 30	29.59	41	39	W.		a little cloudy
	11 . 0	29.48	38	37			cloudy & Starlight

Figure 2.7 A page of temperature values (in degrees Fahrenheit) and other weather observations taken three times daily from 4 to 10 January 1815, at the Radcliffe Observatory, Oxford. The outdoor and indoor temperatures are listed in the third and fourth columns, respectively.

Temperature measurements taken during any given day, such as those in Figure 2.2, could be summarized in several ways. For instance, we could choose to record only the maximum temperature, or only the minimum temperature. Alternatively, we could decide to record the temperature at a given time of day, say 09.00 hours or 12.00 hours (noon). Another option would be to average all of the temperature readings. As long as we are consistent and don't change methods, then a day-to-day record of temperature will always be meaningful.

2.2.1 Hot city nights

With a carefully chosen site, and a standard way of recording daily temperature, a long series of daily temperatures should reveal whether any changes have occurred. We must be grateful to the many dedicated people who painstakingly recorded daily temperatures in past centuries, often just out of personal interest in the world around them. Little could they have known how crucial their measurements would be to later generations trying to understand global environmental problems. But before looking at the global temperature record, it is instructive to consider one of the longest temperature records for a single site in north America. This is the sequence of annual mean surface temperatures for Toronto (Canada) started in 1780. Part of this is displayed in Figure 2.8.

This graph employs two conventions that are often used when displaying historical climate data. The first is to plot the calendar year on the horizontal time axis. The second convention is that the vertical axis plots the *difference* between the annual mean surface temperature and some standard reference temperature, in this case the 50-year mean surface temperature for Toronto over the years 1901 to 1950. So, a value of 2 °C on the vertical axis indicates that the annual mean temperature was 2 °C higher than the 1901–1950 mean. Likewise, a value of –2 °C indicates a value 2 °C lower than the 1901–1950 mean.

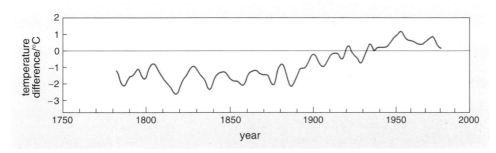

Figure 2.8   Changes in the annual mean surface temperature of Toronto since 1780. The temperatures are shown as differences from the 1901–1950 mean, which appears as a horizontal line. This diagram shows the overall trend of the data as a curve, rather than the individual data points.

Notice further that the annual mean temperature value for each year does not appear as a point on the graph. Instead, the sequence of values has been converted into a 'smoothed' curve, which helps to bring out the underlying pattern of temperature change since 1780. The way this is done is discussed later in Box 2.3, *Smoothing a graph to bring out a trend*, but for now the point to note is that the annual mean surface temperature of Toronto has fluctuated rather than stayed at a constant value. The vertical difference between successive peaks and troughs is the size of these fluctuations and amounts to about 1 to 2 °C. The horizontal distance between the successive peaks and troughs reveals the time intervals between them — which is typically 10 to 20 years. Perhaps more striking is the longer term variation revealed by the graph.

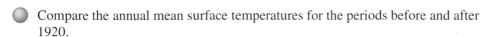 Compare the annual mean surface temperatures for the periods before and after 1920.

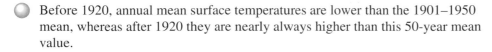 Before 1920, annual mean surface temperatures are lower than the 1901–1950 mean, whereas after 1920 they are nearly always higher than this 50-year mean value.

The exciting question we must now ask ourselves is whether the transition from relatively cool to relatively warm annual mean temperatures, which seems to have taken place between about 1890 and 1950, is a manifestation of global warming.

Before jumping to conclusions, remember that we are dealing with just one site and for all we know there may be other places where the temperature *decreased* over the same time. Furthermore, we are dealing with the temperature record of a large city, and you may know that cities tend to have their own 'urban climate', distinct from the surrounding countryside. Could it be that Figure 2.8 is revealing the local climate effects of a growing city rather than an effect of global significance? Clearly this is an important question to resolve if scientists are to reach correct conclusions about global temperature changes.

The intriguing observation that the temperatures in a city are often slightly higher than in neighbouring countryside was first made by Luke Howard, an English pharmacist. His pioneeringly detailed study of climatic conditions in London led him to write, in 1820:

> But the temperature of the city is not to be considered as that of the climate; it partakes too much of an artificial warmth, induced by its structure, by a crowded population and the consumption of great quantities of fuel.

Howard's words summarize his measurements, which showed a higher temperature within London than outside London. He also stated that city temperatures are not representative of natural conditions, and he put forward three possible explanations for his observation. The explanations are still open to scientific debate, but the basic observational evidence is indisputable. For example, Figure 2.9 shows the urban and rural temperature records for one 24-hour period starting at 12.00 hours (noon).

Figure 2.9 Graph showing the temperature variation at an urban site and at a nearby rural site over a 24-hour period.

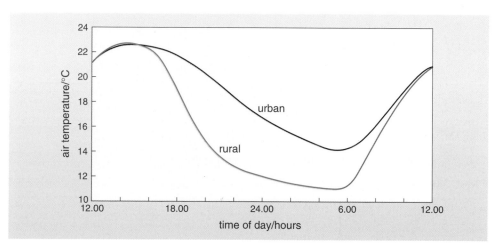

Question 2.5 (a) Describe any similarities between the two curves in Figure 2.9.

(b) Summarize the main difference between the urban and rural temperature records in Figure 2.9. ◀

In general, the centres of most large cities are up to a few degrees warmer than the surrounding region. If you live in or near a city you might like to investigate this by making some measurements yourself or with the help of friends who live nearby. As Luke Howard discovered, urban areas are characterized by an 'island' of warmer temperature in a surrounding 'sea' of cooler temperature, so the anomalous temperature of a city is referred to as an **urban heat island**.

To express the discrepancy between urban and rural temperatures, it is logical to define the 'urban heat island intensity' for a particular city as the urban temperature minus the rural temperature, i.e.

urban heat island intensity = urban temperature – rural temperature   (2.4)

This is the difference between the two curves in Figure 2.9, and it clearly changes during the course of a day.

- At what time of day is the urban heat island intensity at its greatest?

- During the night; in the case of Figure 2.9, the temperature difference is largest at about 21.00 hours.

The warming and cooling patterns seen in Figure 2.9 indicate that cities cool down during the night more slowly than do country locations. This is largely because building materials, such as concrete and road surfaces, lose heat more slowly than vegetation and open ground. For the same reason, cities also warm up more slowly than do country locations.

The implications of the urban heat island intensity for temperature records from meteorological stations located within cities become clear when we see, from Table 2.3, that the size of the city influences the size of its maximum urban heat island intensity. (For a given city, the urban heat island intensity varies from day to day, depending on factors such as wind speed, and is at its maximum under calm and cloudless skies.)

Table 2.3   Maximum urban heat island intensity for four European cities of different sizes.

City	Population at time of temperature measurements	Maximum urban heat island intensity/°C
Lund, Sweden	50 000	5.8
Malmo, Sweden	275 000	7.4
Vienna, Austria	1 870 000	8.0
London, UK	8 500 000	10.0

Question 2.6   If a particular settlement grows in population, and hence the area covered by roads and buildings increases, what will happen to that settlement's urban heat island intensity? What will happen to its mean temperature? ◀

Perhaps you can see what this is going to mean for the interpretation of Toronto's temperature record (Figure 2.8). The population of Toronto grew from 241 in 1797 to 181 200 in 1880, and to 2.8 million in 1976. So, at least some of the temperature increase can be attributed to a growing heat island effect. It therefore becomes important to avoid any such effect where a view of regional temperature change is sought. Luckily, the longest continuous temperature record for anywhere on the Earth has avoided this particular problem; it is the subject of the next section.

2.2.2 The temperature record for central England

There is a remarkable temperature record that extends back to January 1659, for lowland areas of central England. It starts with a number of thermometer readings and general diary entries on weather conditions, which the English meteorologist Gordon Manley (1902–1980) painstakingly collated and interpreted to produce monthly mean temperatures for a representative site. The oldest records he had to deal with comprise diverse readings from different places, taken over different periods of time, using thermometers of varying accuracy, placed in different sites (shade, indoors, outdoors) and read at different times of day. Standardizing the data to produce figures that can be considered representative and comparable from year to year took very careful assessment. Some measurements had to be discarded as unreliable. The documents describing conditions before 1720 are sometimes sketchy, so Manley could estimate mean temperatures for each month only to the nearest degree Celsius. The more reliable data for later years are thought to be good to the nearest 0.2 °C. Daily temperatures representative of central England are available from 1772 onwards. Nowadays, temperature measurements from meteorological stations at Squires Gate Airport (Blackpool), Ringway Airport (Manchester), Rothamsted Agricultural Research Station (Hertfordshire), and Malvern (Worcestershire) are averaged to update this unique record.*

So what does the central England temperature record reveal? Figure 2.10 is a graph of the annual mean surface temperature for every year between 1659 and 1995. The most obvious conclusion we can reach from this plot is that every year is slightly different from the one before. For the period 1659 to 1995, the mean surface temperature is 9.2 °C with most years being within 1 °C of this value. At first glance it appears that the temperature has fluctuated randomly about the mean, but look closer.

● How do the annual mean surface temperatures in the most recent 30 years of the record compare with those of the first 30 years?

○ Most recent years are above the long-term mean of 9.2 °C, whereas the earliest years often lie below the long-term mean.

Figure 2.10 The central England temperature record from 1659 to 1995. Each year is represented by a single dot giving the annual mean surface temperature for that year. The 1659–1995 mean temperature of 9.2 °C is indicated by the horizontal line.

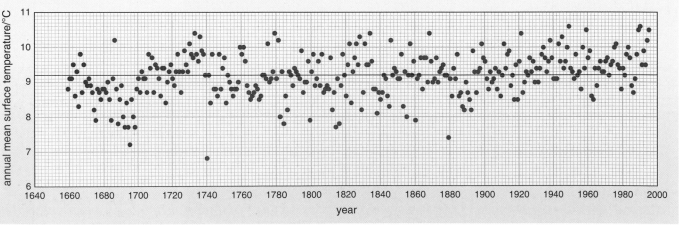

* Every three months the latest results are reported in the monthly magazine *Weather*, published by the Royal Meteorological Society.

Deciding whether the difference between the first 30 years and the last 30 years is just an accidental consequence of comparing temperatures from a randomly fluctuating sequence, or if there has been an overall warming since records began, requires some discussion. Because the data are so scattered, deciding if there is any long-term tendency for the temperature to change — i.e. a trend in the temperature record — would be helped if some of the year-to-year fluctuations could be smoothed out. One way of carrying out this smoothing is outlined in Box 2.3, *Smoothing a graph to bring out a trend*.

Box 2.3 *Smoothing a graph to bring out a trend*

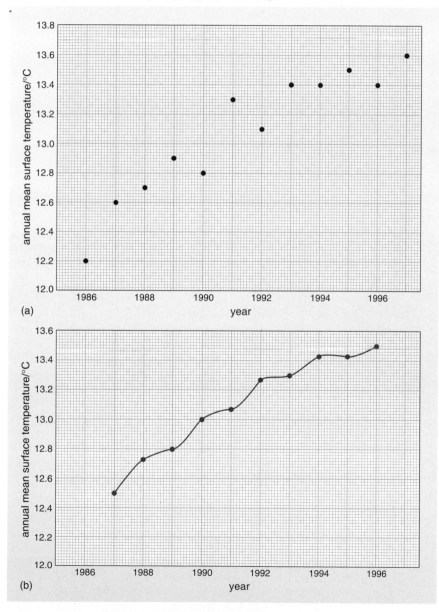

(a)

(b)

Figure 2.11   (a) Fictitious data showing a sequence of annual mean surface temperatures. (b) The data in (a) after smoothing.

Consider the sequence of annual mean surface temperatures in Figure 2.11a. For this invented record, the sequence from year to year is a bit ragged but the overall trend is clearly a general increase. In real data, it is usually not so easy to see the trend and this is where the technique known as smoothing is applied; its effect can be illustrated with the data in Figure 2.11a, as follows.

⬤ Calculate the mean surface temperature for the years 1986–1988 inclusive.

⬤ We use Equation 2.1. The three temperatures are found by reading horizontally across to the vertical (temperature) axis. They are 12.2 °C, 12.6 °C and 12.7 °C and their sum is 37.5 °C. The three-year mean is thus $\frac{37.5\,°C}{3}$, i.e. 12.5 °C.

This value is now plotted on Figure 2.11b at the central year of the set of three years — 1987. We then move on to the years 1987–1989 in Figure 2.11a, calculate the three-year mean, and plot it at 1988. This procedure is followed until we reach the end of the data. The result is shown in Figure 2.11b. The sequence is less ragged and the trend is even clearer. This can be emphasized by drawing a smooth curve through the newly calculated sequence of points.

If we take the years in larger groups, for example five at a time, the smoothing effect is greater.

Smoothing reduces the significance of unusually hot or cold years and so clarifies any long-term changes. In the case of the central England temperatures, smoothing produces the curve shown in Figure 2.12. You should be able to recognize that:

- the smoothed temperature fluctuates on a time-scale of 10 to 25 years;

- from the start of the record until about 1700, the smoothed data lie below 9.2 °C and (from Figure 2.10) few years had an annual mean surface temperature greater than 9.2 °C;

- since about 1900, the smoothed data all lie above 9.2 °C.

Figure 2.12 The trend of mean annual surface temperature for central England between 1659 and 1995. The 1659–1995 mean temperature of 9.2 °C is indicated by a horizontal line.

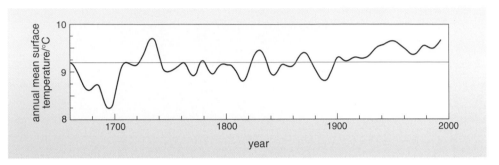

Viewed as a whole, the central England temperature record reveals warming of about 1 °C between the late 1600s and the late 1900s. The change of about 1 °C per 300 years amounts to an average of a third of a degree per century, but with a period of rapid warming between 1690 and 1730 (where the graph rises steeply), and a period of more gradual warming since about 1900. Although the central England temperature record is unaffected by urban heat islands, we need to consider whether the warming it shows is a purely local phenomenon or whether it is representative of an overall warming of the Earth's entire surface.

2.2.3 The historical record of the GMST

Having gained an appreciation of the care required in making measurements, the methods for reducing them to mean values, and the thought needed to make informed interpretations of the measurements, we can now extend our investigation to the history of the GMST. Attempts to determine whether the GMST was changing gathered impetus in the 1980s and, needless to say, required the averaging of data from many land-based and maritime measurements. Sufficient data exist to make confident conclusions about the annual GMST for every year since 1861.

At least two groups of scientists started the mammoth task of reducing the many millions of temperature measurements to a sequence of somewhat more than 100 annual GMST values. Each group worked independently and used slightly different criteria for deciding which measurements were the most reliable, which were unaffected by urban heat islands, and how best to deal with parts of the world with a sparse distribution of weather stations. Nonetheless, their results revealed essentially the same conclusion. In Figure 2.13 we show the difference between the GMST for each year and the 30-year GMST for 1961–1990, which is 15 °C (certainly closer to 15 °C than to 14 °C or 16 °C).

At the start of this section we set out to discover whether the GMST has been constant or has varied. In Figure 2.13 we now have the information with which to address this issue; concentrate for now on the individual data points on Figure 2.13.

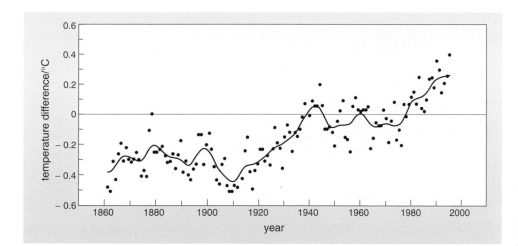

Figure 2.13 The difference in annual GMST from the 1961–1990 mean (15 °C), showing the annual data between 1861 and 1995 and the smoothed trend. (The results are from a study by scientists at the Meteorological Office and the University of East Anglia. These results are used by the Intergovernmental Panel on Climate Change, an international body of scientists who advise governments about the natural and human influences on the world's climate.)

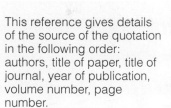

Note that this calculation involves the subtraction of a negative number; you will find that this is discussed in *SGSG* *Maths Help, Section 2, and on the Block 1 CD-ROM in 'Handling negative numbers'.

○ What is the approximate difference in GMST between the first and last year?

○ In 1861, the GMST was about 0.5 °C below the reference 30-year mean (1961–1990), whereas the 1995 value was about 0.4 °C higher than the reference value. The change from the 1861 value to the 1995 value therefore amounts to 0.4 °C – (– 0.5 °C) = 0.9 °C, i.e. an increase of about 0.9 °C.

The most obvious features brought out by the smoothed curve in Figure 2.13 are two periods of sustained warming and two periods in which the GMST fluctuated without any overall warming or cooling trend. Deciding when the fluctuations end and the warming begins is open to debate, and if you get a chance to discuss Figure 2.13 with other students don't be surprised if you reach slightly different conclusions. Writing in 1986, and using data up to 1984, here is how the original authors of the first published version of Figure 2.13 described their results in the international scientific literature:

> The results show little trend in the nineteenth century, marked warming to 1940, relatively steady conditions to the mid-1970s and a subsequent rapid warming. The warmest 3 years have all occurred in the 1980s.
>
> (P.D. Jones, T.M.L. Wigley and P.B. Wright, 'Global temperature variations between 1861 and 1984', *Nature*, 1986, vol. 322, p. 430)

This reference gives details of the source of the quotation in the following order: authors, title of paper, title of journal, year of publication, volume number, page number.

According to the smoothed version of the GMST record (Figure 2.13), the GMST increased by some 0.7 °C between 1861 and 1995.

○ What is the average rate of warming (in °C per century) between these dates?

○ There are 134 years between 1861 and 1995, so a rise of 0.7 °C in 134 years is 0.7 °C/134 years, which is 0.005 °C per year or 0.005 °C × 100, i.e. 0.5 °C, per century (to one significant figure).

Although the trend is one of overall warming since 1861, the rate has not been constant. Also, the temperature change, and the rate of change, have not been the same everywhere on the Earth. Near the Equator, the rate of warming has been less than 0.1 °C per century, whereas in the Arctic and Antarctic the rate is close to 1.5 °C per century.

*Northedge, A., Thomas J., Lane, A. and Peasgood, A. (1997) *The Sciences Good Study Guide*, The Open University.

As we hinted in Section 1, the implications of these temperature rises are potentially worrisome and we'll give them the consideration they deserve in Section 10. Exactly how worrisome depends partly on discovering whether the recent trend in Figure 2.13 is the beginning of a real long-term increase in temperature or just part of a ripple on a series of erratic temperature changes. This is very important because it has implications for predicting future temperatures and climates. To increase the reliability of our predictions, and to increase our understanding of the Earth's surface temperature, we need to find ways of inferring temperatures for times *before* thermometers were in existence. The next section will involve us in the scientific detective work needed to obtain information about ancient temperatures and will enable us to extend curves such as Figure 2.13 backwards in time over very long periods of prehistory.

2.3 Summary of Section 2

The mean of a set of measurements is the sum of the measurements divided by the number of measurements.

The global mean surface temperature (GMST) is calculated (Equation 2.3) from the surface temperatures measured over a year at many sites around the world. If 30 consecutive years are averaged we reduce the effects of rogue years and emphasize long-term trends. The 30-year GMST for 1961–1990 is 15 °C.

Historical records (avoiding variable urban heat island effects) indicate an irregular rise in the annual GMST over the past 100 years. This overall trend is more obvious after smoothing the data, and amounts to an approximate warming rate of 0.5 °C per century. The local warming rate depends on latitude, being least near the Equator.

Conclusions such as these can be reached only by careful gathering of measurements, and critical assessment of the techniques used and of the quality of the data (e.g. the number of measurements used to obtain a mean value, or possible spurious effects such as the growth of urban heat islands). Only after collecting these basic observations is it sensible to start looking for significant trends. You can reflect that, in this section and particularly in Activity 2.1, you will have practised some of the skills associated with gathering reliable data and then interpreting them in a scientific way to reach a conclusion.

Any measured value has an uncertainty associated with it. Random uncertainties lead to scatter of measurements about the 'true' value, whereas systematic uncertainties lead to an offset of the measurements from the 'true' value. Measurements with small random uncertainties are said to be precise, and measurements with small systematic uncertainties are said to be accurate.

Measurements should be quoted with an appropriate number of significant figures. The value 16.4 °C is quoted to three significant figures, and this indicates that there is some uncertainty in the final digit.

The Earth's surface temperatures in the distant past

3

In this section we set out to discover the climatic conditions, particularly temperature, that prevailed in Britain (and indeed the world as a whole) at times before any written reports. To do this we must rely on climate-sensitive clues that have been left behind from times past. Just as archaeological artefacts shed light on prehistoric cultural conditions, we require some sort of ancient remains that indicate ancient temperature conditions.

If we think about the various types of climate around the Earth then it is clear that there is a connection between the climate of a region and the landscape, plant life and animal life of that region. For example, a photograph showing red sand dunes extending for as far as the eye can see suggests that we are looking at a hot desert region. Similarly, tropical rainforests contain an enormous range of animals and plants, many of which can survive only in that hot, wet environment. Thus, monkeys and rubber trees inhabit tropical forests rather than polar regions where the temperature is so low that permanent ice-caps and **glaciers** — slowly moving rivers of ice — characterize the scenery (see title page).

About 200 years ago, scientists began to realize that an area's past climate could sometimes be inferred from particular features of the landscape, or from the remains of plants and animals that had lived and died there but were now preserved as fossils. It is the record of ancient temperatures, and the techniques used to read the record, that are the subject of this section.

3.1 Glaciers past and present

We start with a headline from *The Scotsman* newspaper that rocked Britain's scientific establishment on the morning of 7 October 1840:

> Discovery of the Former Existence of Glaciers in Scotland, especially the Highlands, by Professor Agassiz

Reading this headline today prompts the same questions as a Victorian reader might have asked: What evidence is the discovery based on? How cold was it at the time of the glaciers? How long ago were there glaciers in Scotland? Why was this discovery newsworthy? Who was Professor Agassiz?

Jean Louis Agassiz was a professor of Natural History at the University of Neuchâtel in Switzerland, and he took a particular interest in the glaciers in his native Alps. On a visit to Britain in 1840, he convinced two contemporary British scientists, William Buckland and Charles Lyell, that many of the landscape features in Scotland matched the features being formed 'before his eyes' by the action of glaciers in the Alps of Europe. They agreed that this was evidence that northern Britain had recently been glaciated, but most other scientists at that time found this startling conclusion too revolutionary to accept — after all, there are no glaciers in Britain today. Prior to this glacial theory, most (including Buckland) had accepted the account in the Old Testament of a world-wide flood (Noah's flood) and believed that the sand, gravel and clay that blanket much of Britain were evidence of this great flood. By about 1860, however, most of those who had weighed up the evidence were of the opinion that glaciation had indeed produced many landscape features and also much of the sand, gravel and clay. In the face of actual physical evidence for the new glacial theory, the cherished connection with Noah's flood was abandoned by most scientists. This is an example of how one theory falls out of favour and is discarded when new evidence in support of another theory comes to light.

In the 150 years or so since the glacial theory was proposed (initially as a hypothesis), more evidence has been amassed and found to be consistent with it. (See Block 1, Section 7.1 for a discussion of theories versus hypotheses.) To answer the first question inspired by the newspaper headline — what evidence is the discovery based on — we adopt the strategy of first studying the ways in which present-day ice-caps and glaciers determine landforms, and then show some examples of these characteristic landforms from Britain. Also bear in mind the questions we posed about the temperatures during the glaciation, and the age of the glaciation, for we'll address these too.

3.1.1 Glacial environments of the present day

A glacier can be thought of as a 'river' of ice but, unlike rivers of water, glaciers are typically hundreds of metres or more deep. Another difference is that glaciers flow extremely slowly; typical speeds of glaciers are just 0.3 metre per year to 600 metres per year.

Question 3.1   Express these glacier speeds in metres per second, in scientific notation to an appropriate number of significant figures (see Box 2.1). Write the unit in the commonly abbreviated form (see Block 1, Box 7.1). ◀

In spite of these low speeds, ice-caps and glaciers erode the rock over which they flow, transport the eroded debris away and deposit it elsewhere. In some areas erosion is the predominant process, whereas in others deposition is more important. If we consider glaciated areas in terms of the relative importance of these effects it is possible to recognize the following four types of area, or zone, arranged in the way shown in Figure 3.1.

Figure 3.1   A cross-section of a glaciated region and its surroundings. This diagram is a schematic slice through a part of the Earth affected by glaciation. Boundaries between zones are gradual ones. The labels on this figure are explained in the text.

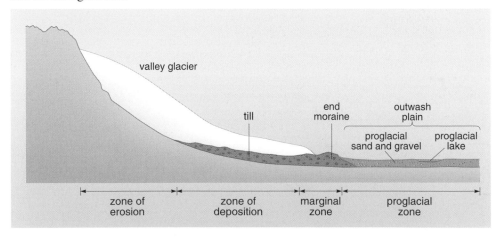

The zone of erosion

Where snow accumulation is greatest a thick layer of ice develops, establishing an ice-cap or glacier, which moves very slowly under its own weight. Large ice-caps are usually referred to as ice-sheets; an example is the Antarctic ice-sheet, which has a maximum depth of over 4 km and covers 12.5 million square kilometres

(12.5 × 10⁶ km²) (units of area were discussed in Block 1, Box 4.2). Elsewhere, glaciers can be less than 1 km² in area. Some of the smallest are confined to valleys, although other valley glaciers spill out from the edges of ice-sheets (see title page).

Beneath the thickest parts of glaciers, the slowly moving ice scrapes against the bare rock, scouring debris away from the ground and carrying it along within the ice. The erosive power of a glacier moving slowly down a valley is enormous. Erosion acts over the floor and sides of the valley to carve a broad **U-shaped valley** (Figure 3.2b). A fast-flowing river, on the other hand, erodes the floor of a valley, resulting in a V-shaped valley (Figure 3.2a). The shapes of the valleys in Figure 3.2 are different because they formed in different ways — one by the action of flowing water, the other by the action of flowing ice.

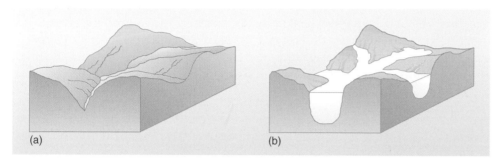

(a)   (b)

Figure 3.2 A mountainous region that experiences erosion by fast-flowing rivers develops a landscape characterized by V-shaped valleys (a). This contrasts with the case in a much colder climate (b) where valley glaciers are present and erode U-shaped valleys.

The zone of deposition

Towards the end of glaciers, large amounts of rock debris, ranging in size from house-sized boulders to dust a few thousandths of a millimetre across, are dumped from the ice and accumulate beneath the active glacier. This muddled mixture of rock particles is called **till** and occurs as mounds, sheets or sinuous ridges called **moraines**, which are left behind when the ice eventually melts; Figure 3.3 shows an example.

Figure 3.3 The moraine in the foreground of this picture was deposited when the valley was filled by a large glacier; the remnants of this Alpine glacier are seen in the background.

The marginal zone

At the very end of glaciers the ice is melting, releasing water and rock debris. Some of the water that emerges from the glacier's front can also come from streams or rivers that flow within or beneath the glacier. Although the escaping water may be travelling rapidly it does not have sufficient strength to carry away the larger fragments of rock so these remain near the front of the glacier, forming an end moraine.

The proglacial zone

This is the area extending outwards in front of the glaciated region. Here, fast-flowing meltwater carries particles of sand and gravel over an outwash plain, forming a complex area of shifting river channels (Figure 3.4). Small lakes can become established in local depressions, and many of the smaller rock particles may settle out from the water to form layers of mud, clay or silt on the bottom of these proglacial lakes.

Figure 3.4 A part of the expanse of gravel that has been deposited from rivers flowing rapidly from the melting glacier visible in the distance. This example of a proglacial zone is on the island of Svalbard (Spitzbergen) in the Arctic Ocean.

3.1.2 Glaciers in Britain's past

Glaciers, and glaciers alone, are responsible for forming landscape features such as U-shaped valleys, moraines, and the types of sand, gravel and clay deposits found in proglacial zones. It follows that an area where such features are observed, but where no glaciers presently exist, must once have been affected by the action of glacial ice. It was this train of thought which Buckland, Lyell and Agassiz followed some 150 years ago when they proposed that Scotland had once been covered by ice. The next step of logic is that the climate must have been considerably colder than at present for glaciation to have been possible. Let's look at the evidence for ourselves.

Look at Figure 3.5, which shows a view of Glen Rosa on the Isle of Arran.

○ What is the evidence that the valley in Figure 3.5 was *not* carved by the stream currently flowing down the valley floor?

○ Glen Rosa is a U-shaped valley (Figure 3.2b) and must, therefore, have been cut by a valley glacier, perhaps not too dissimilar from those on the title page.

Figure 3.5   Glen Rosa, Isle of Arran, western Scotland.

You may have seen other examples of U-shaped valleys in the Scottish Highlands, and elsewhere in the UK, for example the English Lake District or Snowdonia. In all cases the distinctive shape of these valleys indicates that these upland areas were once covered by slowly moving ice. Deposits of till are also common across these areas and other regions of Britain, again implying the former presence of glaciers. But was the whole country under ice?

Only southernmost Britain is free from deposits of till, and this is taken as evidence that glaciation did not reach that far south. Another set of observations that bears on this is shown in Figure 3.6. Ailsa Craig is a distinctively shaped island in the Firth of Clyde (Figure 3.6a). The rock that forms Ailsa Craig is also distinctive, being a particularly decorative type of granite that is unique to the island. However, boulders of this unusual granite are found in many places far to the south of Ailsa Craig (Figure 3.6b). Why these rocks come to be more than 300 km away from their source can be explained by the action of ice transport, because only ice is capable of carrying large boulders over long distances. Such boulders, which have been transported (by natural processes) far from their site of origin, are called **erratics**. The distribution of Ailsa Craig erratics shown in Figure 3.6b implies that the ice that transported them moved southwards, but apparently it did not reach much farther than South Wales. This fits reassuringly with the southern limit of till; it is always satisfying when more than one line of evidence leads to the same conclusion.

(a)

(b)

Figure 3.6 (a) The granite island of Ailsa Craig in the Firth of Clyde is about 1.3 km across and 340 m high. (b) Erratics of Ailsa Craig granite have been found far from their place of origin as shown by the blue dots.

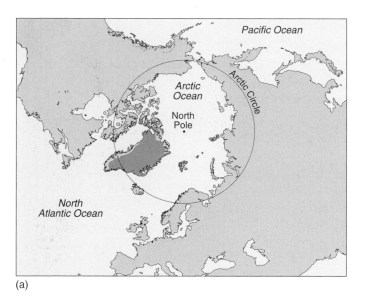

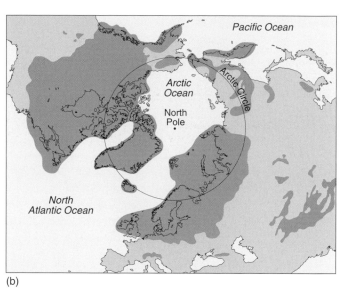

(a)

(b)

Figure 3.7 The deep blue areas on these maps show (a) the present-day extent of northern hemisphere ice-sheets and (b) the greatest extent of ice in the past (about 18 000 years ago).

Using the sorts of evidence we have been looking at, it is possible to recognize signs of glaciation over an area that extends far beyond the present-day limit of ice-sheets (Figure 3.7). This indicates that the Earth's climate was once significantly different, with colder conditions prevailing in Britain and elsewhere. During that time, Britain was cold enough to be mostly covered by permanent ice, and its landscape must have looked similar to that found today in arctic Norway and eastern Greenland (title page). But you may have started to wonder what the temperatures were in those ancient times, or how they changed over time. These topics can be addressed by studying fossils, as the next section will reveal.

Question 3.2   Explain in about 50 words why, in any one region of the Earth, you would *not* expect to find V-shaped valleys at high altitudes and U-shaped valleys at low altitudes. ◄

3.2   Evidence from ancient organisms

We began this block by considering the effects of a decrease or increase in surface temperature and speculated about how these changes might alter the types of crop and other plant growing in a region. Looking back in time, the flourishing of English vineyards in the Middle Ages has been used to suggest that average summer temperatures were warmer by 0.7 to 1.0 °C than in the early 20th century. But how can we look even further back in time?

To discover the types of plant and animal that once inhabited an area, and then infer the climatic conditions that must have prevailed in order for these organisms to have flourished, requires us to study fossils. A **fossil** is evidence of any ancient animal or plant, usually preserved in stone but sometimes found in other types of material, such as peat or amber; Figure 3.8 shows two examples. Presumably the dinosaur in Figure 3.8a was living in the climatic conditions that suited its way of life (breeding behaviour, food supply, etc.) but because dinosaurs are extinct we have no precise way of knowing what those climatic conditions were. For the fossil tree (Figure 3.8b), we can be fairly safe in assuming that the climate must have been within the range of conditions under which trees live today. For example, in terms of temperature, trees survive only where the mean summer temperature is greater than about 10 °C.

(a)

(b)

Figure 3.8   Some examples of fossils. (a) An excavation of a dinosaur skeleton from rocks about 100 million years old in Niger, central Africa. (b) These fossil tree trunks in Western China were alive 150 million years ago; today the area is a desert, but clearly the climate was wetter when the trees were alive.

3.2.1 Pollen

Plant fossils range in size from tree trunks to microscopic pollen grains. Many plants shed pollen from the male parts of their flowers, and the pollen is carried on the wind or by insects to the female parts of flowers where fertilization occurs. It is by this process that the plants produce their seeds. The spring and summer air becomes heavily laden with pollen, as hay fever sufferers know only too well, and a mature tree may produce many tens of millions of pollen grains each year. Needless to say, a single pollen grain is tiny; its size can be measured in millionths of a metre (see Box 3.1, *The micrometre*).

Box 3.1 **The micrometre**

For things as small as pollen grains it becomes convenient to use a new unit — the micrometre, sometimes called the micron. The prefix **micro** indicates 'one millionth' in the way that milli means 'one thousandth' (Block 1, Box 3.1). The symbol for a micrometre uses the Greek letter μ (mu, pronounced 'mew'), to indicate the micro part, in front of m for metre: hence μm is the symbol for micrometre. There are several ways of expressing a micrometre:

$$1\,\mu m = \frac{1}{1\,000\,000}\,m = \frac{1}{10^6}\,m = 10^{-6}\,m$$

How many micrometres are there in a millimetre?

We know that $1\,\mu m = 10^{-6}\,m$, so there are $10^6\,\mu m$ in 1 m. Likewise, $1\,mm = 10^{-3}\,m$, so there are $10^3\,mm$ in 1 m. This means that $10^3\,mm = 10^6\,\mu m$, so $1\,mm = \frac{1\,000\,000\,\mu m}{1\,000} = 1\,000\,\mu m$. In words, there are one thousand micrometres in one millimetre.

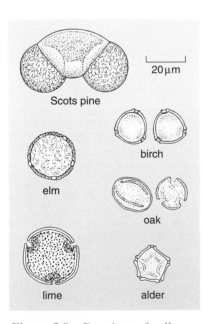

Figure 3.9 Drawings of pollen grains from different types of tree. Note the scale bar indicating that these small grains are only 20 μm or so across.

Most pollen grains never reach the flowers for which they were intended, but instead fall to the ground or onto the surface of lakes and streams. Pollen grains can be deposited in the silt accumulating on the bottom of lakes or in peat accumulating in bogs and become preserved as fossils. Because plants produce huge numbers of pollen grains, just one spoonful of peat can contain many thousands of pollen grains from the trees, shrubs and grasses in the vicinity of the peat bog. Furthermore, because each type of plant produces pollen with a unique shape and surface pattern (Figure 3.9) it is possible to identify the range of plant types that have contributed to a given sample of pollen. Thus, whereas a rare fossil tree stump preserved in a bog reveals the identity of one type of plant that once grew in some ancient landscape, a mere handful of peat from the same bog contains a whole variety of pollen types, which reveals the range of plants that were present in that region.

Question 3.3 Figure 3.10 shows a number of pollen grains taken from a 140 000 year old sample of Essex clay. Compare their shapes with those of the pollen grains in Figure 3.9. Do you think that the local trees included oak and Scots pine, or elm and lime? ◄

3.2.2 Pollen diagrams and ancient climates

The usefulness of fossil pollen to the scientist is that the types and proportions of pollen in a sample, such as Figure 3.10, can be compared with those produced by vegetation growing in present-day climates. The climate at the time the sample was formed can then be inferred. This brings us back to the main thread of this section, which is the pattern of temperature change on the Earth through time.

By collecting a series of pollen samples of different ages from a given area or site, and inferring the climate that produced each sample, we can arrive at a picture of how

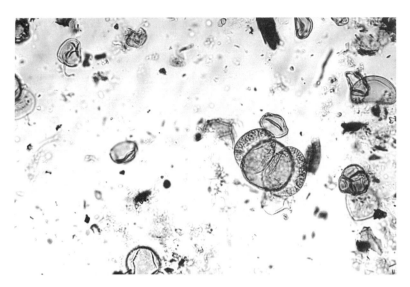

Figure 3.10   Pollen grains that have been carefully separated and extracted from a sample of clay from Marks Tey, near Colchester, Essex, seen magnified by a microscope.

climate (or just temperature) changed over time. Samples of different ages are obtained by taking samples from different depths below the surface of a peat bog or lake bed. In the case of the peat bog, successive layers of organic matter grow and decay on the surface, progressively burying older peat. Likewise on the lake bed, the most recently deposited silt covers previously deposited layers of silt. So, by boring down into the deposits it is possible to extract a column, or core, of material, which will be a layer-by-layer record of sedimentation and pollen accumulation over time (Figure 3.11). The deeper the sample in the core the older it will be. The age of a sample, in years, is worked out using specialist techniques such as radiocarbon dating (borrowing a method used by archaeologists to date ancient wooden and cloth artefacts), but it is the results rather than the dating techniques that are of interest here.

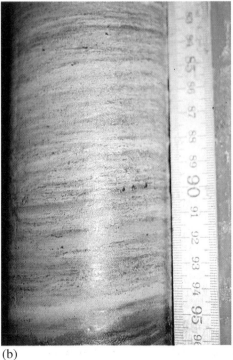

Figure 3.11   (a) Scientists obtaining a core of sediment from the bed of Lake Igelsjoen, Sweden. (b) Part of the extracted core showing alternating dark and light layers of silt that were deposited 5 000 years ago. The scale is marked in centimetres.

(a)

(b)

Samples of a few cubic centimetres are extracted from the core at accurately measured distances from the end that had been at the Earth's surface. Each sample is then carefully treated to liberate the pollen grains. The pollen from each sample is examined under a powerful microscope, and every grain of pollen is identified (as in Question 3.3) and counted. Several hundred grains are identified and counted in each sample and the proportions of the different types calculated. The rewards of such a painstaking gathering of facts are the insights obtained into past vegetation and climate.

Evidence of changing climate is indicated by changes in the proportions of different pollen types as we progress upwards through a core. It is easiest to make sense of the results by using a diagram, rather than a table containing a long list of the numbers, representing the percentages of different types of pollen grain at different depths in the core. An example is Figure 3.12, which shows how the amount of birch pollen (expressed as a percentage of the total tree pollen present) varies with the depth in a core taken in the bed of a lake at Hockham Mere in Norfolk; the scale on the left-hand edge of the diagram gives the depth. Figure 3.12 may at first seem hard to interpret, but it is basically just another graph, so you need to look carefully at the scales and the axis labels. This graph may look odd because the vertical scale of depth increases as you go down the page, whereas graph scales usually increase upwards. Also, you may be used to the horizontal axis being longer than the vertical, not the other way around as here. However, the way the axes are arranged should help you to picture the core as a long stack of samples extracted from the ground. In this case, the vertical scale shows that the core goes to a depth of a little over 8 m. From other evidence, we know that the deepest layers were deposited some 10 000 years ago. Shallower layers are progressively younger towards the top. The percentage of birch pollen present at any depth is read from the horizontal scale, and the variation in the percentage is emphasized by the convention of using shading.

Question 3.4   Study Figure 3.12 carefully.

(a) Approximately what percentage of the tree pollen in the samples from between 6.5 and 7.5 m depth is birch pollen?

(b) What is the approximate percentage of birch pollen in the upper half of the core?

(c) Has the percentage of birch pollen increased or decreased with time? ◀

At Hockham Mere, pollen grains are also found from Scots pine, elm, oak, lime and alder trees. The percentages for these can be plotted in the same way as in Figure 3.12. Doing this and setting the results out side by side gives Figure 3.13. A plot, such as this one, showing the proportions of different pollen types through a vertical sequence of samples, is called a **pollen diagram**. The diagram for tree pollen from Hockham Mere (Figure 3.13) shows some striking changes in the proportions of pollen types and hence in the proportions of different trees growing near the site over the past 10 000 years or so.

When you answered Question 3.4 you may have noticed that the decrease in the percentage of birch pollen occurs between 6.5 and 5.5 m depth. Because we are dealing with percentages, rather than the absolute number of pollen grains, a decrease in the percentage of one component must be balanced by increases in the percentages of other components so as to account for the full 100% of the grains present in any one sample.

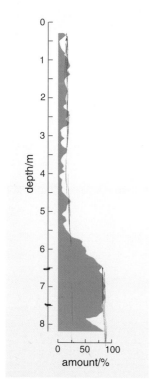

Figure 3.12   A diagram showing how the amount of birch pollen (as a percentage of the total tree pollen present) in samples from a core taken at Hockham Mere varies with depth.

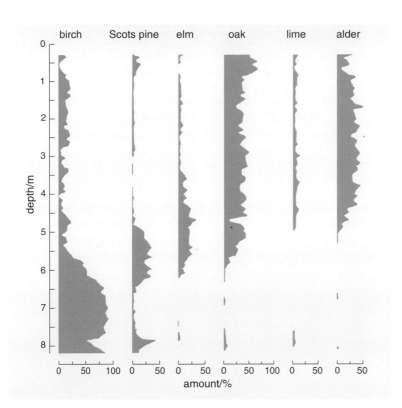

Figure 3.13   A tree pollen diagram from Hockham Mere.

○ As the percentage of birch pollen declines, what increases?

○ Scots pine, elm and oak pollen all become more abundant in the depth interval between 6.5 to 5 m (Figure 3.13).

So, the pollen diagram shows birch giving way to Scots pine, elm and oak, with lime and alder making an appearance at about 5 m depth. We also see Scots pine declining in abundance at around 5 m, and elm declining at around 3.5 m. To think about what these observations mean, and whether they are related to temperature, answer the following question.

○ From your general knowledge, which of the following factors can influence the types of tree that can grow in a given area: temperature; rainfall; the amount of human pollution in the atmosphere (e.g. resulting in acid rain); other activities of human civilization; altitude (i.e. the height of the area above sea-level)?

○ *All* of the listed factors can, to some extent, influence what types of tree (if any) can grow.

For example, the relatively cold, wet climate of mountainous northwest Scotland sustains birch and Scots pine forest — or did until much of the land was cleared for grazing sheep — whereas the natural woodland of comparatively warm, dry lowland southeast England sustains oak and beech. Acid rain may kill trees, although some types are more susceptible to pollution than others. Conifers, for instance, are often more damaged by air pollutants than deciduous trees because the needles of conifers, which are retained all year round, act as efficient air filters, trapping pollutants within the plant.

Let's now consider which of the five factors could have changed during the 10 000 year period in order to bring about the changes indicated by the pollen diagram in Figure 3.13.

A significant change in the altitude of Hockham Mere is unlikely over this time-scale, and anyway there is no evidence that this took place, so we can dismiss this possibility. Pollution such as acid rain is a phenomenon that became important only in the 20th century, so this cannot explain the much older changes in vegetation observed in Figure 3.13. Archaeological evidence for the spread of Neolithic farming activities and forest clearance coincides with the time level at which elm declines in importance (about 3.5 m depth), but there is no evidence for ancient Britons removing or introducing particular types of tree *before* then. We must conclude that these earlier changes in vegetation were caused by changes in the climate. By comparing the climatic conditions under which woodlands of different compositions grow at present, it has been found that the changing composition of woodland in the vicinity of Hockham Mere indicates a warming over time. As the temperature increased, Scots pine, elm, oak, lime and alder became established. The different rates at which these trees appeared, and the decline of birch and Scots pine, reflect additional biological factors related to the processes of plant migration and competition, but the main stimulus for change was a change in climate.

Extending this approach to look at even longer pollen records of temperature variation simply requires cores that penetrate into older layers. The most remarkable such core, providing a record over the past 140 000 years, is from Grande Pile in the Vosges region of eastern France. Figure 3.14 is a pollen diagram for this core, simplified to show only the total percentage of tree pollen present; pollen grains from other plants make up the remainder of each sample.

Question 3.5   On the basis of Figure 3.14, which parts of the Grande Pile core were formed during the coldest periods? (*Hint*   Think about the temperature conditions required for trees to thrive which we noted just before the start of Section 3.2.1.) ◄

The interpretation of pollen records to reveal insights into prehistoric climates is a scientific triumph. But so far in this section we have been taking only a qualitative approach; in other words, we have been avoiding putting numbers on temperatures. We have also been rather cavalier in assuming (rather than confirming) that climate plays an important role in determining which plants can grow in any given area. This seems a reasonable assumption based on general knowledge, and indeed a careful assessment does reveal that climate really is important. In particular, the climatic variables that influence plant growth and reproduction are the most important, and these include winter temperature, summer temperature and rainfall (which influences soil moisture). This means that we can now become quantitative and start to assign particular temperature values to times long before thermometers were invented, complementing the historical information in Section 2.

The method of assigning temperatures requires the calculating power of a computer, but basically relies on making observations of present-day climates and flora (the mix of plant types present in an area) so that the temperature conditions required for particular sets of plants to thrive can be identified. The results can then be applied in reverse, starting with a mix of plants found in an ancient pollen sample and inferring the temperatures appropriate for those plants. Applying these techniques, the 140 000 year pollen record from Grande Pile has been converted into the 140 000 year record of long-term mean temperature displayed in Figure 3.15, where a 'long term' is a

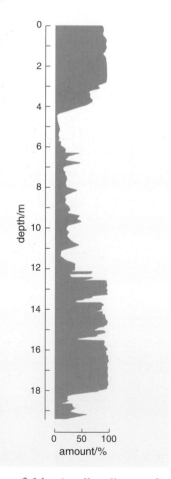

Figure 3.14   A pollen diagram for Grande Pile, France, showing the percentage of tree pollen.

period much longer than a year. Notice that the results are shown as a shaded band rather than a thin line. This is because there is some uncertainty in estimating the temperature for each pollen sample, and the result must be expressed as falling within a likely range of temperatures rather than as a definite value.

Figure 3.15 is plotted in the same style as the pollen diagrams, that is, with age increasing downwards. The results from the oldest, deepest, part of the core are found towards the bottom, and the results from the youngest, shallowest, part are found towards the top. This convention conveys the idea that information about older times is more deeply buried in the original core. The horizontal axis shows that temperature increases to the right.

Figure 3.15 reveals a number of cold periods separated by warmer periods, all of different durations. Mean temperatures during the warmer periods were similar to those of today. The colder periods had temperatures some 6 to 10 °C colder. The transitions between cold and warm periods occurred over relatively short time-spans, so these were periods of rapid temperature change.

Question 3.6   According to Figure 3.15, what (approximately) would the long-term mean temperature have been in this part of France (a) 1 000, (b) 10 000, (c) 40 000 and (d) 100 000 years ago? ◄

⬤ Considering the past 140 000 years as a whole, is the mean temperature higher, lower or the same as the recent long-term mean temperature?

◯ Figure 3.15 shows short periods where the temperatures were the same or slightly higher than at present. For longer periods the mean temperature was much lower than recently. Overall, the mean temperature in this part of Europe was lower than recently.

Putting this another way, we have found that although we take the recent temperatures for granted, they are unusual with respect to the conditions over the past 140 000 years.

Activity 3.1   Summarizing the use of pollen diagrams

Section 3.2.2 described the use of fossil pollen to infer the temperatures at the time the fossilized plants were growing and also described some of the results from this technique. This activity aims to help you consolidate your understanding of the text, by summarizing in your own words how pollen diagrams are used to reconstruct ancient temperature records. ◄

3.3   Ice ages past and future?

In the last two sections we discussed the origins of Britain's glaciated landscapes and evidence from fossils that indicated that temperatures in Europe were once significantly lower than those of today. We also found that temperatures have varied during at least the past 140 000 years. To reflect on the ways by which this conclusion was reached, tackle the following question.

Question 3.7   Why does the study of fossil pollen samples provide more information about past temperatures than does the study of landscape features? ◄

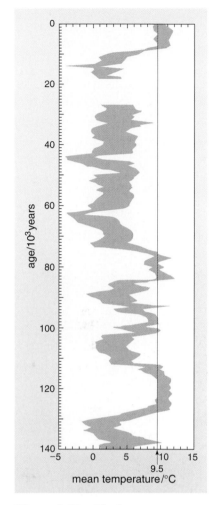

Figure 3.15   The long-term mean temperatures inferred from the Grande Pile pollen record. The gap in the record is a consequence of the sediment and pollen in this part of the core having become disrupted and mixed during its original deposition to such an extent that a meaningful temperature cannot be calculated. The long-term mean temperature at Grande Pile in modern times is 9.5 °C. Note that the vertical axis is labelled 'age /10³ years'. This means that the numbers read from the vertical scale must be multiplied by 10^3 years; for example 20 on the scale means 20×10^3 years.

The answer to Question 3.7 summarizes two of the techniques used to estimate ancient temperatures. The most informative methods are those that allow temperature values to be inferred from readily measured observations (e.g. pollen identification) of *dateable* samples. Many such methods rely on fossils of organisms that were sensitive, in known ways, to the temperature conditions at the time they were alive. As well as fossil pollen from plants, it's also possible to use fossil insects, shellfish, and microscopic marine plants and animals to work out temperatures, both on land and in the oceans. As we said in Section 2, there can be more to measuring temperature than 'just sticking a thermometer in the air'. Collecting the samples, preparing them for analysis, making the observations, dating the samples to find their age, and finding a reliable method for converting the observations into a temperature value are all part of the process and demand the utmost care. Piecing together the hard-won evidence to build a picture of the Earth's surface temperature has presented us with clear indications that the Earth's climate has not always been the same as it is today.

The reconstructed temperature history of the Grande Pile region of France over the past 140 000 years (Figure 3.15) looks complex. Between about 75 000 and 10 000 years ago the mean temperature was consistently lower than that of today. Fossil evidence from many other places also indicates relatively cold conditions during the same interval. This was a **glacial period**, and much of Britain, northern Eurasia and northern America were glaciated (Figure 3.7b).

Evidence from older fossils found elsewhere allows the Earth's temperature record to be extended further back in time. This has revealed that in the last 2.4 million years (a period nearly 20 times longer than that covered by the Grande Pile record), there have been several glacial periods lasting for up to hundreds of thousands of years, separated by shorter **interglacial periods** with more temperate conditions. The total collection of glacial and interglacial periods constitutes an **ice age**. So, according to this pattern, the relatively warm conditions we are enjoying in today's climate are because we are experiencing an interglacial period that started about 10 000 years ago. This is part of an ice age that began some 2.4 million years ago. During an ice age the world is not permanently locked in the grip of ice-sheets, but it experiences periods of glaciation interspersed by more temperate conditions.

The Earth is much much older than a few million years, however, so what can we say about conditions in the more distant past? Tracking the Earth's surface temperature far back into the history of the Earth is a challenge to scientists because the record of ancient conditions preserved in rocks (the **geological record**) is much more patchy. Some segments of the record are missing, others are hard to interpret because the connection between temperature and fossil life is unknown or only qualitatively known. Generalizing information about regional conditions to get a global picture presents another set of problems. Putting every scrap of evidence together has led to the graph shown in Figure 3.16, which shows how the Earth's surface temperature has fluctuated during the whole of Earth history. Notice that the time axis counts backwards from the present day to the very earliest history of the Earth — an amazing 4 600 million years ago (see Box 3.2, *Geological time*). The horizontal axis distinguishes only between cold and warm relative to the present temperature, because of the difficulties in assigning temperature values. Note that the last 2.4 million years occupy a very small space at the top of this diagram, so the scale of this graph is inadequate for clearly showing the interglacial and glacial periods within the current ice age. Much older ice ages can be recognized in the geological record by

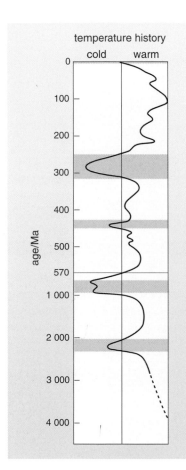

Figure 3.16 A generalized temperature history of the Earth relative to the current GMST (the vertical line), but note that the temperature scale is qualitative. The times when major ice ages occurred are identified in blue. As in Figure 3.15, age increases downwards; the scale on the vertical axis changes at 570 Ma because the geological record is poorly preserved in rocks older than 570 Ma.

key lines of evidence, such as widespread deposits of glacial till, and their ages are indicated by shading on Figure 3.16. Such ancient ice ages are recognized in rocks as old as 2 300 Ma and they appear to occur roughly every few hundred million years, and last for several tens to hundreds of millions of years.

Box 3.2   Geological time

As you will see in later blocks, the Earth has existed for an extremely long time — about 4 600 million years. The purpose of this box is to summarize the shorthand ways of handling the large numbers needed to describe geological time.

Rather than writing out a string of zeros, or the words million (for 10^6) and billion (for 10^9), it is convenient to introduce the following abbreviations:

1 000 years, or 10^3 years, is written as 1 ka (kiloannum)

1 000 000 years, or 10^6 years, is written as 1 Ma (mega-annum)

1 000 000 000 years, or 10^9 years, is written as 1 Ga (giga-annum)

The same kilo, **mega** and **giga** prefixes are used in many other circumstances to denote 10^3, 10^6, and 10^9, respectively. Examples from Block 1 and everyday experience are kilometres of distance and megabytes or gigabytes of computer memory.

So the age of the Earth can be written in a host of ways: for example, 4 600 000 000 years, 4.6×10^9 years in scientific notation, 4 600 Ma or 4.60 Ga.

Note that 'annum' is Latin for 'year' and the abbreviation 'a' is used with kilo, mega and giga only when dealing with geological time. For all other cases in this course we use 'year', or the abbreviation 'y'. (In some other publications, you may find million years abbreviated to My rather than Ma.)

Question 3.8   Express the following times in years to two significant figures using scientific notation: (a) 2.1 Ga; (b) 570 Ma; (c) 140 ka.◀

Question 3.9   Express (a) 19 500 years in ka, and (b) ·115 000 years in ka and Ma, to three significant figures.◀

Given the fluctuating climate patterns in Figures 3.15 and 3.16, it seems reasonable to expect that at some time in the future the present interglacial period will come to an end and be replaced by a glacial period. Eventually the current ice age will itself finish. Even further in the future another ice age might become established. A variable GMST has been part of the Earth's natural behaviour for as long as we can tell. So, is the warming that we recognized in Figure 2.13, and which many people are concerned about, just another aspect of the Earth's normal behaviour? To attempt to answer this important question requires us to identify those factors that can influence the GMST. This is the subject of the next few sections.

3.4   Summary of Section 3

Certain landscape features in Britain and elsewhere, including U-shaped valleys, deposits of till and the distribution of erratics, can be attributed to the effects of glacial erosion and deposition, implying past temperature conditions much colder than today.

The make-up of plant communities is sensitive to climatic conditions, including temperature. Records of prehistoric plant communities preserved as fossil pollen can be used to estimate the mean temperature at the time the plants were alive. Fossil pollen from different depths in cores taken through peat bogs and lake beds reveals how the proportions and identities of the plants changed through time, and hence how climate changed through time.

The longest continuous pollen record is from France and spans the last 140 000 years, but by piecing together many different fossil records from separate places a much longer temperature history can be established. This reveals that we are living in an ice age that started some 2.4 million years ago. Throughout this ice age, cold glacial periods have alternated with shorter interglacial periods when the climate has been warmer. The most recent glacial period ended about 10 000 years ago, and we live in an interglacial period.

Ice ages of several tens to hundreds of millions of years duration have occurred at intervals throughout at least the last 2 500 million years of the Earth's history.

What determines the Earth's GMST? Overview

4

You have seen that there is overwhelming evidence for past changes in the global mean surface temperature (GMST). As well as there being great *scientific* interest in these changes there is also great *practical* interest. This is because an understanding of past variations should help us to predict future variations, including those in the very near future, in which we or our immediate descendants will live. Therefore, for scientific and practical reasons, it is important to explore *why* the temperature has varied in the past. Our starting point is to consider the factors that determine the GMST, a subject that will occupy us for the whole of Sections 4 and 5.

The GMST depends on the various ways in which the Earth's surface gains energy, and on the various ways in which it loses energy. In Section 4.1 we will take a broad look at these gains and losses, and at how they determine the GMST. But before this, we must discuss energy, and Box 4.1, *Energy and power*, introduces you to this concept.

Box 4.1 Energy and power

Energy

Energy is one of those words in common use with a variety of everyday meanings, encapsulated in such phrases as 'I'm full of energy today'. 'Energy' also has a precise scientific meaning; indeed, it is one of the most important concepts in the whole of science.

● Note down two or three phrases in which you include the word 'energy' in an *everyday* sense.

○ Some possible examples are: 'Where do those children get their energy from?'; 'I haven't got the energy to get up'; 'Sweets are full of energy'.

None of the everyday usages of the word 'energy' is very precise but they all encapsulate the notion that energy enables activity to take place. This is also at the heart of the scientific notion of energy. **Energy** is a physical property possessed by an object, and is a measure of the capability of the object to 'make things happen'. In order for things to happen some of the energy in the object must be transferred to some other object. Here are some examples.

One type of energy is inherent in the motion of an object, such as a football hurtling through the air. If you happen to be in the way and it knocks you over then you will have no difficulty in agreeing that some of the football's energy of motion was transferred to you, and that this made something happen.

Another type of energy is that which we get from food. For example, a spoonful of sugar provides energy that we can utilize when we eat it. Energy from food keeps us alive by maintaining our body temperature and by making it possible for our muscles to function.

Energy also has an effect on temperature. When we burn gas under a pan of water, energy is transferred from the flame to the water, and as a result the temperature of the water increases. Similarly, when an electric kettle is used to heat water, energy is transferred to the heating element from the electric current running through it, and energy is then transferred from the element to the water. Thus, a common consequence of transferring energy to an object is to cause its temperature to rise: this is an important feature which you met briefly in Block 1, Section 4.1.3, and which you will meet several times later in this block and in subsequent blocks.

Because energy is a physical property possessed by an object it can be measured, and it therefore has a unit of measurement. Though there are very many forms of energy they can all be measured in the same unit. The SI unit of energy is called the **joule**, named after the British scientist James Prescott Joule (1818–1889) who made major contributions to developing our concept of energy. The symbol for the joule is J.

The precise definition of the joule would take us much deeper into the topic of energy than we need to go at this stage. It is, however, useful for you to get some 'feel' for the size of a joule, and the domestic electric kettle provides it. Such a kettle can hold about two litres of →

water. If the kettle is well insulated to avoid heat loss, and the water is heated from 20 °C to 100 °C, then about 6.7×10^5 J of energy will have been transferred from the heating element to the water. The joule is therefore a rather small unit by everyday standards.

Question 4.1   (a) If the two litres of water were heated from 20 °C to only 30 °C, would the amount of energy needed to heat the water be greater than, less than, or equal to 6.7×10^5 J?

(b) If only one litre of water was in the kettle, would the energy needed to heat the water from 20 °C to 100 °C be greater than, less than, or equal to 6.7×10^5 J? ◀

The kitchen contains many other examples of amounts of energy, notably in the energy ratings on packets of food. Nearly all prepacked food tells you how much energy it will give you if you eat it. This is usually quoted as the number of kilojoules per 100 grams of the food, a kilojoule (kJ) being a thousand joules. Figure 4.1 shows an example of a food packet.

INGREDIENTS

MAIZE, BROWN SUGAR, PEANUTS, SUGAR, HONEY, MALT FLAVOURING, SALT, NIACIN, IRON, VITAMIN B$_6$, RIBOFLAVIN (B$_2$), THIAMIN (B$_1$), FOLIC ACID, VITAMIN B$_{12}$.

NUTRITION INFORMATION

		Typical value per 100g		Per 30g Serving with 125ml of Semi-Skimmed Milk	
ENERGY	kJ	1650		750 *	
	kcal	390		180	
PROTEIN	g	7		6	
CARBOHYDRATE	g	82		31	
(of which sugars)	g	(34)		(17)	
(starch)	g	(48)		(14)	
FAT	g	3.5		3.0 *	
(of which saturates)	g	(0.6)		(1.5)	
FIBRE	g	2.5		0.8	
SODIUM	g	0.7		0.3	
VITAMINS:		(%RDA)		(%RDA)	
THIAMIN (B$_1$)	mg	1.2	(85)	0.4	(30)
RIBOFLAVIN (B$_2$)	mg	1.3	(85)	0.6	(40)
NIACIN	mg	15	(85)	4.6	(25)
VITAMIN B$_6$	mg	1.7	(85)	0.6	(30)
FOLIC ACID	µg	167	(85)	60	(30)
VITAMIN B$_{12}$	µg	0.85	(85)	0.75	(75)
IRON	mg	7.9	(55)	2.4	(17)

* For whole milk increase energy by 100kJ (25kcal) and fat by 3g.
* For skimmed milk reduce energy by 70kJ (20kcal) and fat by 2g.
Contribution provided by 125ml of semi-skimmed milk:-
250kJ (60 kcal) of energy, 4g of protein, 6g of carbohydrates (sugars), 2g of fat.

Figure 4.1   A label from a food packet. The energy provided is 1650 kilojoules (kJ) per 100 grams.

You might like to inspect the food packets in your kitchen for further examples of the energy provided by different types of food. You are likely to see that (as in Figure 4.1) the energy is also given in another unit, the kilocalorie (kcal). This is *not* an SI unit of energy and will not be used in this course.

That's the end of our brief introduction to energy. It is a concept that will be developed throughout the course and with which you will gradually become familiar, so don't worry if it seems a bit elusive or mysterious at this stage.

Power

Like energy, power is another of those words with everyday meanings that also has a precise scientific meaning. Its scientific meaning is derived from the scientific concept of energy. **Power** is the *rate* at which energy transfer takes place, i.e. it is the amount of energy transferred in one unit of time. This can be expressed in words as

power = energy transferred per unit of time

$$\text{power} = \frac{\text{energy transferred}}{\text{time taken}} \qquad (4.1)$$

The SI unit of time is the second, and the SI unit of energy is the joule, so the power is the number of joules transferred per second. For example, suppose that 500 joules of energy are transferred from one object to another in 20 seconds. Then the energy transferred per second $= \frac{500\,\text{J}}{20\,\text{s}} = 25$ J/s or 25 J s^{-1}.

So, in this case, the rate of energy transfer, or power, is 25 J s^{-1}. You can see that the SI unit of power is J s^{-1}.

There are many circumstances in which it is the rate of energy transfer that matters and not the total amount transferred. For example, if we want to know how rapidly the temperature of a litre of water will rise by 1 °C, it is not enough to know that 4 200 J will raise it from 20 °C to 21 °C. We need to know how rapidly the energy will be transferred, or supplied to the water.

◯ If 4 200 J are supplied to the water in one second, how long will it take for the water temperature to rise by 1 °C?

◯ 4 200 J is the amount of energy needed to raise the temperature by 1 °C, so if it is supplied in one second then the temperature rise also takes one second.

On the other hand, if 4 200 J are supplied over two seconds then it will take two seconds for the 1 °C rise. If the energy is supplied over 0.1 second the rise takes only 0.1 second.

● What are the rates of energy supply (the power) in these three cases?

○ If 4 200 J are supplied in 1.0 s then the rate is 4 200 joules per second, i.e. 4 200 J s⁻¹. If 4 200 joules are supplied in 2.0 s, then

$$\text{rate of energy supply} = \frac{4\ 200\ \text{J}}{2.0\ \text{s}} = 2\ 100\ \text{J s}^{-1}$$

As you might expect, the rate is halved. If 4 200 joules are supplied in 0.10 second, then

$$\text{rate of energy supply} = \frac{4\ 200\ \text{J}}{0.10\ \text{s}} = 42\ 000\ \text{J s}^{-1}$$

It is rather cumbersome referring to the rate of energy transfer or power in joules per second. What we need is a unit that equals a joule per second. There is such a unit: a joule per second is called a **watt**, symbol W. This is exactly the same watt as that used in specifying the power requirements of electrical appliances. However, the watt is a general unit for the rate of all forms of energy transfer, not just those involving electricity. The watt is named after the Scottish engineer James Watt (1736–1819) who, amongst other things, made major improvements to the design of steam engines, the main source of technological power in his day.

● Express 4 200 J s⁻¹ in watts.

○ This is 4 200 watts, or 4 200 W.

Typical domestic electric kettles have power ratings of 1 000 W to 3 000 W, i.e. the electric element in a particular kettle will transfer energy to the water in the kettle at a rate somewhere in this range. In the domestic setting it is usual to quote power in kilowatts, kW, where 1 kW = 1 000 W.

Question 4.2 You have seen that a well-insulated kettle with two litres of water requires 6.7×10^5 J to raise the temperature of the water from 20 °C to 100 °C. Suppose this takes 335 s. Calculate the power rating of this particular kettle. (Ignore heat losses from the water to the surrounding air and the energy required to heat the kettle itself.) ◄

You are now ready to consider the various rates of energy transfer — the rates of energy gain and loss — that determine the GMST. Though 'power' is an equivalent term to 'rate of energy transfer' and is shorter, we will normally use the longer term because it is more descriptive.

4.1 A balance of energy gains and losses

The GMST depends on the rate at which the Earth's surface gains energy, and the rate at which it loses energy. Note that, strictly speaking, by 'surface' we mean the actual ground (or ocean) surface but we can extend this to include the air just above it, and this is essentially the same zone for which changes in the GMST were explored in Sections 2 and 3.

The Sun is the ultimate source of almost all the energy gained by the Earth's surface.

All other sources of energy are negligible. The largest is the heat that flows out from the interior of the Earth, but the rate of flow is 2 000 times less than the rate at which the surface gains solar energy. The Earth's surface loses energy by various means. For now we lump them all together to give one overall rate of energy loss. We thus arrive at the highly simplified picture in Figure 4.2.

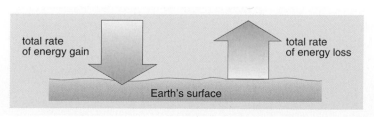

Figure 4.2 Rates of energy gain and loss by the whole of the Earth's surface.

The downward pointing arrow represents the rate at which the whole of the Earth's surface gains energy, and the upward pointing arrow that originates at the Earth's surface represents the rate at which the whole of the Earth's surface loses energy. Note that the width of the downward pointing arrow is equal to that of the upward pointing arrow. This is a pictorial way of showing that the rates of energy gain and loss in Figure 4.2 are equal. A direct and important consequence of this equality is that the GMST is constant. If the rates were not equal then the GMST would change. Thus, if the rate of energy gain were to exceed the rate of loss then the excess energy input would cause a rise in GMST to a new higher value.

⬤ If the rate of energy loss were to exceed the rate of energy gain what would happen to the GMST?

◯ The surface would cool to a lower GMST.

In fact, the rates are not exactly equal every second, and through the day and the year there are moments when the gain slightly exceeds the loss, and other moments when the loss slightly exceeds the gain. However, over a period of a few years the gains and losses largely balance out; for this reason, if the GMST is averaged over a few years then the average is very nearly the same as over the previous few years or the following few. Therefore, the rates of energy gain and loss can be taken as near enough equal when averaged over the short term. Note that these rates can't always have been *exactly* equal, or the GMST would never have varied in the past, yet we know from Sections 2 and 3 that it has.

Let's explore in a bit more detail the relationship between the GMST and the rates of energy gain and loss. This brings us to the analogy of the leaky tank.

4.1.1 The analogy of the leaky tank

The relationship between the GMST and the rates of energy gain and loss at the Earth's surface can be elucidated by considering the behaviour of a very different system — a leaky tank into which water is pouring.

The photos in Figure 4.3 show a tank of water with a tap feeding water in, and a vertical slot in the side of the tank letting water out. The rate at which water is fed into the tank represents the rate of energy gain by the Earth's surface; the rate at which water leaks out of the slot represents the rate of energy loss from the Earth's surface. The level of water in the tank represents the GMST: the higher the level, the higher the GMST.

Figure 4.3a shows a sequence that starts with the tank empty, and the water flowing in at a steady rate. Initially, the leak rate is smaller than the rate of input, so the water level rises. The leak is through the rectangular slot at the side of the tank. As the water level rises there is a greater length of slot to let the water out, and so the leak rate increases, and it continues to increase until the leak rate equals the rate of water input. At this point the water level stops rising, and it stays at the level it has reached. The water level is now in a **steady state**, i.e. the level is not changing. Water is, of course, pouring into and out of the tank, and so we have a *dynamic* steady state rather than a *static* steady state. The crucial condition for the dynamic steady state is that the input and output rates are equal. This equality of rates can be expressed as

input rate = output rate (4.2)

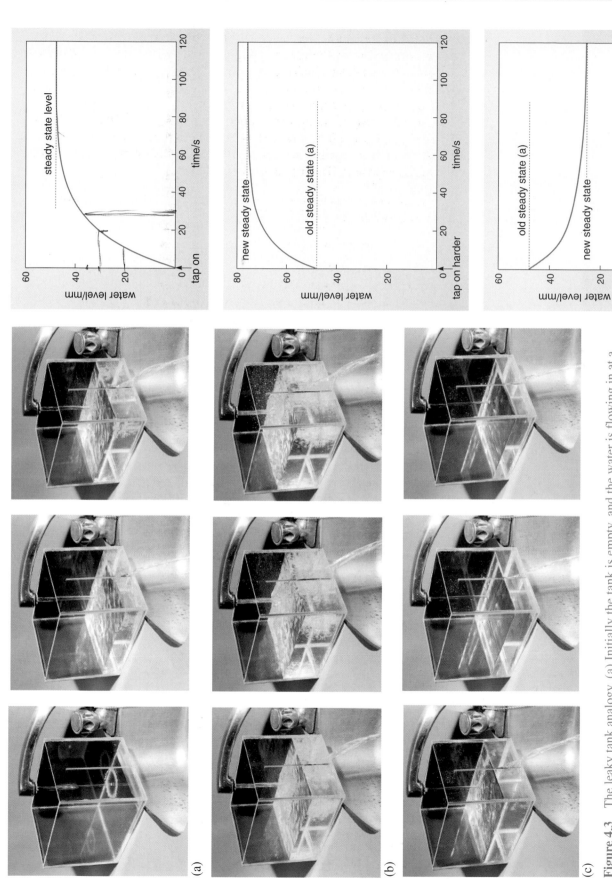

Figure 4.3 The leaky tank analogy. (a) Initially the tank is empty, and the water is flowing in at a certain rate. The water level rises until the leak rate equals the rate of input, whereupon the level becomes steady. (b) The input rate is increased, and the water rises to a new steady level that is higher. (c) The input rate is decreased, and the water falls to a new steady level that is lower.

The graph to the right of Figure 4.3a shows the way the water level changes with time. You can see that in the first 10 seconds after the tap is switched on, the water level rises from zero to 17 mm. In the time interval 10 to 20 seconds after the tap is switched on it rises from 17 to 30 mm, i.e. a further 13 mm in the next 10 seconds.

○ How many millimetres does the water level rise in the time interval 20 to 30 seconds after the tap is switched on?

○ Reading from the graph in Figure 4.3a, it rises from 30 to 37 mm, i.e. a further 7 mm in this next 10 seconds.

Thus as the water level rises, the rate at which the level changes slows down. In the graph this is apparent in the 'bending over' of the line. You can see that ultimately the line flattens off and stays at the same water level — the steady state level. At this constant level the leak rate equals the rate of input.

If we now turn the tap on harder to increase the input rate, then the water level starts to rise again. The leak rate increases until we reach a new steady state, with a higher water level, as in Figure 4.3b. The graph to the right of Figure 4.3b shows this level to be 76 mm. Alternatively, suppose we return to the original steady state at the end of the sequence in Figure 4.3a, but now *reduce* the flow from the tap. The leak rate is now greater that the input rate, so the water level falls. This reduces the leak rate until another steady state is reached, this time at a lower water level, as in Figure 4.3c. The graph shows this level to be 25 mm.

The leaky tank might, or might not, have been thought-provoking. The important point is that it provides a simple, though useful, analogy of the behaviour of the GMST. In the broadest terms, an analogy is a different type of physical system that has properties that in some important way are similar to some of those of the actual system of interest. Analogies are often used as an aid to understanding, and this is the case here where we use a leaky tank as an analogy of the energy gains and losses by the Earth's surface. Let's see how the analogy of the leaky tank provides insight into the behaviour of the real Earth.

In Figure 4.3a we start with the analogy of a cold Earth (the empty tank) with the Sun (the tap) just having been switched on. The surface of the Earth gains solar energy (the water) and so the GMST (the water level) rises. As it does so — and this is a *crucial* point — the rate of energy loss from the Earth's surface increases, i.e. *the higher the GMST the greater the rate of energy loss from the Earth's surface*. The reasons for this relationship between GMST and energy loss rate will be explored in Section 5. For now, the important point is that the GMST rises until the rate of energy loss by the surface equals the rate of energy gain, whereupon, as at the right of Figure 4.3a, a steady state is reached, with the GMST no longer changing. This corresponds to the real situation in Figure 4.2.

Figure 4.3b is analogous to an increase in the rate of energy gain by the Earth's surface, such as would follow an increase in the rate at which energy is emitted by the Sun. The GMST then rises until the loss rate equals the new rate of gain. We then have another situation as in Figure 4.2, but with higher gain and loss rates.

⬤ What is happening to the GMST in the analogy in Figure 4.3c?

◯ In Figure 4.3c the rate of energy gain by the Earth's surface is decreased, so the GMST falls until the loss rate equals the new, lower rate of gain.

Figure 4.4 adds these two new steady state cases to that in Figure 4.2, along with the graphs that show the transition of the GMST from the original steady state in Figure 4.4a to each of the new steady states.

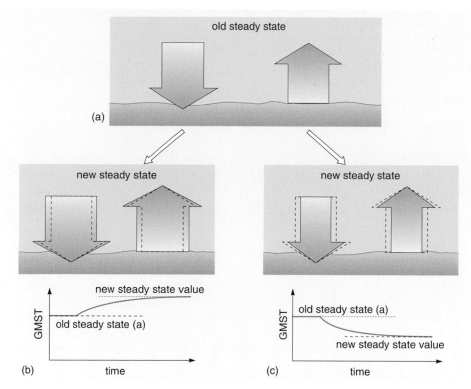

Note that the graphs in Figure 4.4 do not have scales on the axes, but have an arrow on the end of each axis to show the direction in which the quantity (GMST or time) increases. This is done when a graph is drawn to show only qualitavely how two quantities are related.

Figure 4.4 (a) A repeat of Figure 4.2. (b) When the rate of energy gain by the surface of the Earth is increased the GMST rises. (c) When the rate of energy gain by the surface of the Earth is decreased the GMST falls. The width of each arrow is proportional to the rate of energy transfer, and the dashes in (b) and (c) show the sizes of the arrows from (a).

Returning to the water tank analogy, another way to influence the water level is to alter the width of the slot that controls the leak rate. If the slot is narrowed then the leak rate at any water level is less than it was before. If it is widened then the leak rate at any water level is higher than it was before.

Activity 4.1 Modifying the leaky tank

This activity gives you the opportunity to explore the consequences of changing the width of the slot in the leaky tank, and to present the consequences as a written answer illustrated with diagrams and graphs.◀

Activity 4.1 shows what happens when (in effect) there is a change in any of the processes that determine the rate of energy loss from the Earth's surface. The widening of the slot is equivalent to increasing the rate of energy loss from the surface, and narrowing the slot is equivalent to decreasing the rate of loss. In each case the GMST changes until a new steady state is achieved. When the loss rate is increased the new GMST is lower, and when it is decreased the new GMST is higher.

As you will see, the processes by which the Earth's surface gains and loses energy are very different from the processes by which the tank gains and loses water, but the analogy should help you to understand that:

- the rate of energy loss from the Earth's surface increases as the GMST rises, and decreases as the GMST falls;

- a steady-state GMST requires that the rate of energy gain by the Earth's surface equals the rate of energy loss;

- if the steady state is disturbed in any way, and there is no further disturbance, then a new steady state is ultimately established, with a different GMST.

In the next section we shall take a closer look at the energy gains and losses at the Earth's surface.

4.2 Summary of Section 4

The transfer of energy to an object can have a variety of effects. One of these is to cause a rise in the temperature of the object.

Power is the rate of energy transfer. The SI unit for energy is the joule (J), and the SI unit for power is the joule per second (J s^{-1}), also called the watt (W).

The Sun is the ultimate source of almost all of the energy gained by the Earth's surface.

The GMST depends on the rate at which the Earth's surface gains energy, and the rate at which it loses energy. If these two rates are equal then there is a dynamic steady state and the GMST does not change. If the rates are unequal then the GMST will change. The rate of loss of energy from the Earth's surface increases as the GMST rises, and decreases as the GMST falls.

A leaky tank of water is a useful analogy for the energy gains and losses at the Earth's surface, and the corresponding GMST. In this analogy:

- the rate at which water flows into the tank represents the rate at which energy is gained by the Earth's surface;
- the rate at which water flows out of the tank represents the rate at which energy is lost by the Earth's surface;
- the level of the water in the tank represents the GMST.

Activity 4.2   Summarizing the leaky tank analogy

This activity has two purposes. One is to reinforce your understanding of the leaky tank analogy. The other is to give you further practice at extracting the essential points from a section. ◄

What determines the Earth's GMST? A closer look

5

This section starts by examining the energy gained by the Earth's surface when it absorbs solar radiation, and the ways that energy is lost from the surface. We then examine a further energy gain by the surface — radiation from the atmosphere. The section concludes by bringing all the gains and losses together, so that we can identify the various factors that determine the GMST.

5.1 The rate of gain of energy from solar radiation

You have learned that the Sun is the ultimate source of almost all the energy gained by the Earth's surface. Solar energy reaches us across the huge gulf of space that separates us from the Sun. We sense some of this energy with our eyes as sunlight, which would blind us if we stared at the Sun, but which provides us with daylight. We sense some of it with our skin, via the sensation of warmth when we stand in the sunshine.

The energy that floods out from the Sun is called **solar radiation**. 'Radiation' in general terms means something that spreads out (radiates) from a source. There are several completely different types of radiation, but solar radiation is dominated by an extremely important type — electromagnetic radiation. This is introduced in Box 5.1, *Electromagnetic radiation*. You will need to study this box to understand some key ideas later in this section.

Box 5.1 Electromagnetic radiation

As its name implies, **electromagnetic radiation** involves electricity and magnetism, though in quite what way we shall leave for later blocks. It is conventional to divide the full range of electromagnetic radiation into subranges. For example, electromagnetic radiation to which our eyes are sensitive is called, unsurprisingly, **visible radiation**, or light. Another subrange is the electromagnetic radiation detected by our skin when we face the Sun or a fire, and feel the sensation of warmth. This is called **infrared radiation** — the reason for the name will become apparent shortly.

Figure 5.1 includes these two subranges, along with all of the others. The ordering from left to

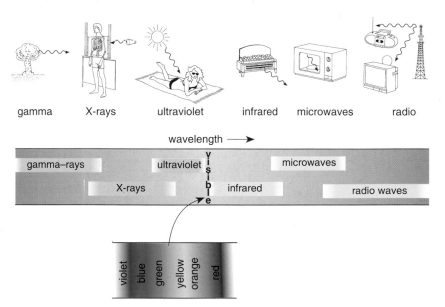

Figure 5.1 Electromagnetic radiation subdivided by wavelength. Note that the wavelength increases from left to right across the figure, so that (for example) infrared waves have longer wavelengths than visible radiation.

53

right in Figure 5.1 is in accord with a property of electromagnetic radiation that increases in value continuously from left to right, with no abrupt changes as we go from one subrange to the next. This property is called the *wavelength* of the radiation in space.

For something to have a wavelength it needs to be a wave. Consider first a familiar example of a wave — ripples on a pond, as

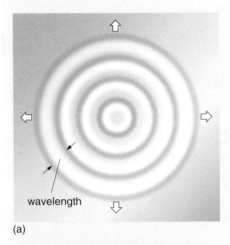

(a)

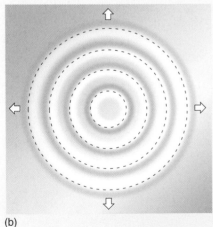

(b)

Figure 5.2 Idealized diagrams of ripples resulting from a stone being dropped into a pond at the point that is at the centre of the pattern. Pattern (a) shows the ripples at a particular instant; pattern (b) shows them a short time later.

in Figure 5.2. These ripples radiate from the centre of the pattern, which could, for example, mark the point where a stone entered the water, thus creating the ripples. The ripples are shown at two instants so that you can see how they move. The dashed circles in Figure 5.2b show where the ripples were a short time earlier (Figure 5.2a). To see the motion in more detail you can create your own ripples in a pond, or even in a basin of water. The length marked '**wavelength**' is the distance between adjacent peaks of the wave. It is also the distance between adjacent troughs.

In the ripples on a pond the waves are variations in the height of the surface of the water. Electromagnetic waves are very different. As their name suggests, they are variations in electric and magnetic effects, though we will have to leave it as vague as that for now, relying on Block 11 to give more detail. Though electromagnetic radiation is a very different sort of wave from ripples on a pond, the notions still apply of the waves spreading out from a source, and of wavelength as a characteristic length over which the wave repeats itself.

There is, however, an important difference. Whereas the ripples in Figure 5.2 are waves on a *surface*, electromagnetic waves can spread through a *volume*, rather like sound waves spreading out from a loudspeaker. This is illustrated schematically in Figure 5.3, where a source is emitting radiation of a particular wavelength. This particular source emits waves uniformly in all directions, and so the waves spread out through three-dimensional space like spherical

shells, as indicated. In the case of electromagnetic waves the volume around the source can be solid, liquid, or gas, but can also be empty space, i.e. a vacuum. This important property of electromagnetic radiation is almost unimaginable — waves that travel through 'nothing'! We shall return to this remarkable property in Block 11. The speed at which these waves travel in empty space is $3.0 \times 10^8 \, \text{m s}^{-1}$, known as the speed of light, and so it takes solar radiation only 500 seconds to travel the huge distance of 1.5×10^{11} metres from the Sun to the Earth.

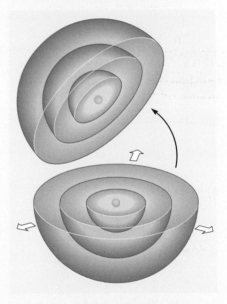

Figure 5.3 Electromagnetic waves spreading out spherically from a source into the space around it, which can be a vacuum. For clarity, the diagram shows the spherical shells opened up to expose the source.

The wavelength of the ripples on the pond in Figure 5.2 is a few centimetres. This is rather a long wavelength by the standards of electromagnetic waves. Electromagnetic waves with wavelengths of a few centimetres are known as microwaves (Figure 5.1). Microwaves occur naturally, but we also generate them with our technology for use in microwave ovens and in communication and radar. Radio waves are the adjacent subrange, and have longer wavelengths than microwaves. They are also used in communication. All of us are familiar with radio and TV aerials that broadcast radio and TV programmes. These aerials are sources of radio waves (TV is broadcast by radio waves!). Indeed, many radios have a tuning scale marked in metres. This is a wavelength scale, with different stations broadcasting their programmes using waves with different wavelengths.

The wavelengths of visible radiation (light) are very short, around 5×10^{-7} m.

- What is this in micrometres?

- A micrometre (μm) is 1×10^{-6} m (a millionth of a metre), so 5×10^{-7} m is 0.5×10^{-6} m, which is $0.5\,\mu$m (Box 3.1).

Light spans the colours of the rainbow. These colours correspond to different wavelengths, ranging from violet light with a wavelength of about $0.4\,\mu$m, to red light with a wavelength of about $0.7\,\mu$m.

- What kind of electromagnetic radiation has wavelengths between those of light and microwaves?

- Infrared radiation (Figure 5.1).

'Infra' is Latin for 'below', so if you imagine turning Figure 5.1 on its side, with red light below violet light, you can see that infrared is 'below red'. Similarly, 'ultra' is Latin for 'beyond', and so ultraviolet (UV) radiation is 'beyond violet' in that it has shorter wavelengths than violet radiation. A well-known effect of the UV component of solar radiation is the chemical one on human skin that leads to a suntan. This is why the information on creams to

prevent sunburn often refers to 'ultraviolet filters' that reduce the intensity of the UV radiation that reaches the skin.

Figure 5.1 also shows X-rays and gamma-rays, electromagnetic radiation with extremely short wavelengths. You may be familiar with the use of X-rays in medicine, and with gamma-rays in association with nuclear weapons and nuclear power stations. X-rays and gamma-rays will not concern us in this block.

That ends this brief look at electromagnetic radiation. Before you move on, you might like to reflect on how well you are handling 'first looks' at concepts about which you will develop an understanding in stages, spread over several months. Electromagnetic radiation is one such concept, energy is another. You may feel frustrated by having to live for a while with partial understanding, but try instead to regard it as a valuable first step, with fascinating further insights to come in future episodes.

Figure 5.3 could represent solar radiation leaving the Sun except in one important respect: solar radiation is not confined to a single wavelength, a point to which we shall return shortly. First we need to concern ourselves with the overall rate at which solar radiation reaches the Earth so that we can explore further this dominant source of energy.

- What is the SI unit with which we should measure the rate at which energy leaves the Sun in the form of electromagnetic radiation?

- The SI unit for the rate of transfer of any form of energy is the watt, so the unit is the watt (or $J\,s^{-1}$).

A large power station generates about 10^9 W of electrical power, and all the power stations in the world generate rather less than 10^{13} W. The Sun is far more powerful: it emits electromagnetic radiation at the prodigious rate of 3.85×10^{26} W. This power is called the **solar luminosity**.

The radiation from the Sun spreads out in all directions, as in Figure 5.3. Some of it encounters the top of the Earth's atmosphere at all places on the Sun-facing side of the Earth, as in Figure 5.4. This side can be represented as a disc-shaped area facing

55

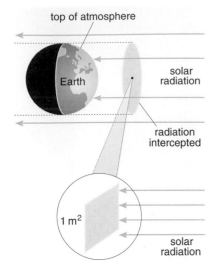

Figure 5.4 The Earth intercepts the amount of solar radiation that falls on the grey disc-shaped area facing the Sun. An area of 1 m² within this disc, shown greatly magnified at the bottom of the diagram, receives (on average) 1 370 W of solar electromagnetic radiation. The Earth is much smaller than the distance to the Sun, and so the rays from the Sun are very nearly parallel.

the Sun, shown pale grey in Figure 5.4. The rate at which this area intercepts solar radiation is obtained from measurements made by means of radiation sensors on satellites in orbit around the Earth. (It is necessary to go into space because the Earth's atmosphere absorbs some solar radiation.) It is found that an area of one square metre facing the Sun, as in Figure 5.4, intercepts 1 370 W of solar electromagnetic radiation. In other words, 1 370 W per square metre, or 1 370 W m^{-2}, are intercepted. This value is an average over recent years, the actual value varying slightly from moment to moment. This average value is called the **solar constant**.

The disc-shaped area in Figure 5.4 that the Earth presents to the Sun is obviously *much* larger than 1 m² — it is in fact 1.27×10^{14} m². The total solar radiation intercepted by the Earth can then be calculated from:

$$\text{total solar radiation} = \text{solar constant} \times \text{area of disc} \tag{5.1}$$

This comes out as 1.74×10^{17} W (Box 6.2 will show you how to multiply quantities in powers of ten notation). The total amount of solar radiation intercepted is also an average, for the same reasons that the solar constant is an average value. Not all of this intercepted radiation reaches the Earth's surface. To see why, we must examine the fate of solar radiation in its passage through the Earth's atmosphere to the Earth's surface.

Question 5.1   (a) Consider a 60 watt electric light bulb, which is in common domestic use. A 60 watt bulb loses energy at a rate of 60 W (60 joules per second). Most of this is in the form of electromagnetic radiation, though some is in the form of heat passing into the surrounding air and into the bulb stem. If the 60 W bulb is shining steadily, then it is in a steady state. At what rate is the bulb gaining energy, and where does this energy come from?

(b) What implication does your answer to part (a) have for what is happening in the Sun? ◄

5.1.1 Solar radiation in the Earth's atmosphere and at the Earth's surface

The Earth's atmosphere has a thickness of a few tens of kilometres. The distance to the centre of the Earth is about 6 400 km, so the atmosphere is a thin veneer, though a vital one for life, and it also has significant effects on the incoming solar radiation. These effects are partly due to the gases that constitute the atmosphere, and partly due to atmospheric aerosols. An **aerosol** is a collection of tiny liquid or solid particles dispersed in a gas, such as water droplets in the atmosphere (inside or outside clouds). Atmospheric dust is another example of an aerosol, in this case consisting of solid particles. An aerosol spray from a can consists of tiny liquid droplets.

In its passage through the Earth's atmospheric gases and aerosols, solar radiation is subject to two different processes that each reduce the amount reaching the Earth's surface. These are contrasted in Figure 5.5. Figure 5.5a illustrates the process of **absorption** of solar radiation by atmospheric gases and aerosols. The essential feature of absorption is that solar radiation is ultimately converted into heat, which causes a rise in the temperature of the atmospheric gases and aerosols.

Figure 5.5b illustrates the other atmospheric process. This is called **scattering**. In this process, atmospheric gases and aerosols do not absorb solar radiation, but redirect it. Scattered radiation travels in all directions. Some escapes back to space, and the rest

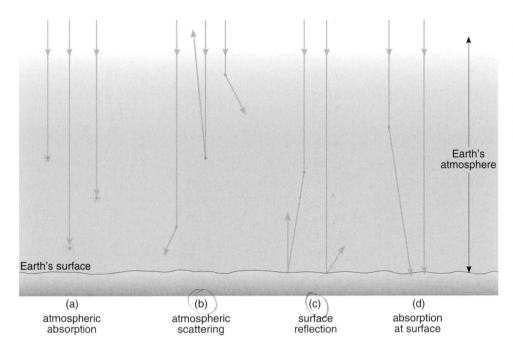

(a) atmospheric absorption

(b) atmospheric scattering

(c) surface reflection

(d) absorption at surface

Earth's atmosphere

Earth's surface

Figure 5.5   (a) The absorption of solar radiation by the Earth's atmosphere. (b) The scattering of solar radiation by the Earth's atmosphere. (c) The reflection of solar radiation by the Earth's surface. (d) The absorption of solar radiation by the Earth's surface.

reaches the Earth's surface, having taken an indirect route to get there. Clouds are particularly good scatterers, but so too are some other aerosols.

Scattering and absorption occur throughout the atmosphere, though particularly in the lower levels where most of the mass of the atmosphere is concentrated, as you will see in Section 6.

The solar radiation that escapes absorption or scattering back to space reaches the Earth's surface. Some of this radiation is scattered from the surface, as illustrated in Figure 5.5c. In this case, because the Earth is so dense, the radiation is not scattered in all directions, but only back into the atmosphere. It is usual to call this process **reflection**, though at heart it is the same as scattering. Different types of surface reflect different proportions. Ice and snow reflect most of the solar radiation that falls on them, whereas the oceans reflect very little.

The radiation reaching the Earth's surface that is not reflected is absorbed (Figure 5.5d). In the oceans this absorption takes place throughout the top few tens of metres of water, whereas on the land it is confined to a much thinner surface layer. Just as in the atmosphere, the absorbed solar radiation gives rise to an increase in the temperature of the surface. In other words, the Earth's surface is *radiantly heated* by the Sun. You will further explore radiant heating later, in Activity 5.1.

Question 5.2   Figure 5.6 is an image of the Earth from space. This image was formed from solar radiation at visible wavelengths that has been scattered by clouds and reflected by the surface.

(a) In one sentence state how you would expect the visual brightness of a region in the image to depend on the proportion of visible solar radiation reflected or scattered by the materials in the region.

(b) From your general knowledge of the Earth, what are the brightly reflecting materials at A and B, and what is the dark material at C? ◄

Figure 5.6 The Earth from space.

Figure 5.7 presents estimates of the average rates of energy transfer that involve solar radiation in the Earth's atmosphere and at the surface. In all cases it is average global totals that are shown, i.e. the global totals averaged over several years. We could have given the values in watts, but we get more manageable numbers in Figure 5.7 if we use an arbitrary unit of power, with 100 units representing the total power in the solar radiation intercepted by the Earth.

⬤ How many watts do 100 units correspond to in Figure 5.7?

⬤ 100 units correspond to 1.74×10^{17} watts (Section 5.1).

Figure 5.7 Rates of energy transfer involving solar radiation in the Earth's atmosphere, and at the Earth's surface. The width of each arrow is proportional to the rate of energy transfer.

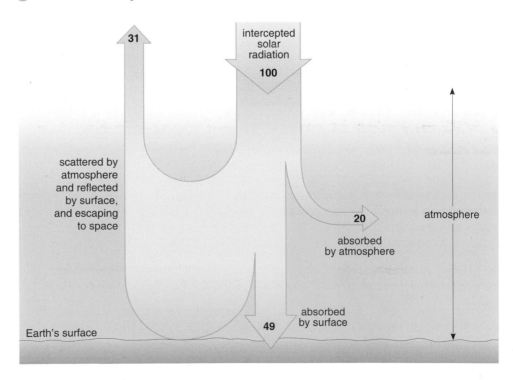

In Figure 5.7, the arrow that sweeps through the atmosphere down to the Earth's surface and returns to space represents the rate at which solar radiation is returned to space through the combined effects of scattering by the whole depth of the atmosphere and reflection by the whole surface (31 units). The arrow that ends in the atmosphere represents the rate at which solar radiation is absorbed by the atmosphere (20 units). (This includes any scattered and reflected radiation that is *subsequently* absorbed by the atmosphere.) The remaining arrow represents the rate at which solar radiation is absorbed by the Earth's surface (49 units).

Question 5.3   From Figure 5.7, express each of the rates (a)–(c) below as a fraction of the rate at which solar electromagnetic radiation is intercepted by the Earth. Convert each fraction into a decimal and then into a percentage. (Note that Box 3.2 in Block 1 shows you how to convert fractions into decimals, and Box 2.4 shows you how to convert fractions into percentages.)

(a) The rate at which solar radiation is returned to space by the combined effects of scattering and reflection.

(b) The rate at which solar radiation is absorbed by the atmosphere.

(c) The rate at which solar radiation is absorbed by the Earth's surface. ◄

One of the quantities that you calculated in Question 5.3 has a special name. The average global rate at which solar electromagnetic radiation is returned to space by the combined effects of scattering and reflection, expressed as a fraction (or decimal, or percentage) of the average global rate at which solar electromagnetic radiation is intercepted by the Earth, is called the **planetary albedo**. The word 'albedo' is derived from the Latin 'albus', meaning 'white'.

Note that the terms 'solar radiation' and 'solar electromagnetic radiation' are used interchangeably in this block.

Having considered energy gains made by the Earth's surface, we shall now turn to energy losses. But first you have the opportunity to carry out an activity to help you consolidate various ideas about the absorption of radiation, and the concept of a steady state.

Activity 5.1   Radiant heating of light and dark surfaces

In this activity you will investigate how two different surfaces warm up when they are heated by a light bulb. This will involve plotting graphs of experimental data; advice on how to do this is contained in the Study File. ◄

5.2   The rates of energy loss from the Earth's surface

There are three major ways in which the Earth's surface loses energy — one is the emission of radiation by the surface, and the other two depend on a process called convection occurring in the atmosphere.

5.2.1   Convection

Convection carries energy away from the Earth's surface through currents of air rising upwards. However, it helps to look at this process first in the simpler case of liquids.

Consider a pan of water at room temperature standing on a switched off electric hot-plate, as in Figure 5.8a. There is no upward or downward motion in the water, and the density and temperature of the water are the same throughout its volume.

○ Recall from Block 1 the definition of density.

○ In Section 4.2 of Block 1 density was defined as

$$\text{density} = \frac{\text{mass}}{\text{volume}} \tag{5.2}$$

Figure 5.8 A pan of water (a) before it is heated, (b) when it is heated from below and showing convection.

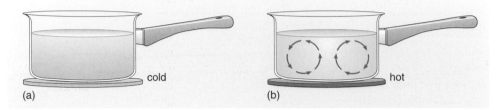

Let's suppose that we now disturb this quiescent state of affairs by switching on the hot-plate. This heats the base of the pan which causes a rise in its temperature, and the base of the pan in turn heats the thin layer of water in contact with it, causing the water's temperature to rise. The water in this layer is heated by a process called **conduction**. This is the transfer of heat from a region of higher temperature (the base of the pan) to a region of lower temperature (the bottom layer of water) because of the direct contact between the two regions. A familiar consequence of conduction is the rising temperature of your hand when you place it against a jug of hot liquid.

The rise in the temperature of the thin layer of water causes it to increase in volume. This is called **thermal expansion**, which is a phenomenon displayed by all liquids, and by solids and gases too. In Box 2.2 you saw that the thermal expansion of the liquid in a thermometer is the basis of its operation.

○ What will happen to the density of the thin layer of water when it expands? (Note that its mass is fixed.)

○ From Equation 5.2, if the mass is fixed but the volume increases, then the quantity on the right of the equation decreases, and so the density will decrease.

The thin layer of water now has a lower density than the water above it. In Section 4.2 of Block 1 you saw that a lower density solid floats on a higher density liquid (ice or wood in water being the Block 1 examples).

○ What will happen to the lower density solid if it is pushed under the liquid?

○ It will rise back to the surface.

You can try this out with an ice cube in water. For two liquids you can try it out with some cooking oil and water. The oil is less dense and will rise to lie above the water.

We therefore expect the warmed water with its reduced density to rise upwards, and indeed it does. In doing so it displaces the overlying cooler, denser water downwards. In principle this could happen in a number of different ways. It could happen at a microscopic scale, with tiny uprising threads of warm water and tiny descending threads of cooler water. It turns out that it happens on a larger scale, and Figure 5.8b shows a typical pattern of motion. A steady cycle is set up, with warmed water rising to the surface, displacing the cooler water downwards where it is warmed in turn and also rises. Meanwhile, the water that had risen has cooled, and will then be displaced downwards by the rising water. Fluid flow driven by temperature differences is called **convection**, and Figure 5.8b shows one example. A somewhat similar pattern is set up in a heated pan of porridge or custard, with the advantage that the pattern (at the upper surface) is readily visible. You should try it: after all, you can always eat the food afterwards.

For the GMST, the relevant feature of convection in a liquid in a pan is that it transfers energy away from the base of the pan at a considerably higher rate than if there were only conduction through the liquid. Imagine what happens if we now replace the heated base of the pan by the radiantly heated Earth's surface, and the water by the Earth's atmosphere. You can see that if conduction of heat from the Earth's surface into the atmosphere in contact with the surface gives rise to convection, then this is a process by which the Earth's surface would lose energy at a considerable rate. In the Earth's atmosphere convection does indeed occur, though it is more complicated than in the liquid in the pan. Recall that in the pan, before we switched on the heat, the water was everywhere at the same temperature and density. In the case of the Earth's atmosphere the density decreases with increasing altitude, and so (usually) does the temperature.

We shall not go into these complications here. The important point is that convection occurs in the atmosphere, and that by this means the Earth's surface loses energy at a considerable rate and the atmosphere gains energy at a corresponding rate. Atmospheric convection can sometimes be seen in the shimmer from the heated air rising from a particularly hot surface such as a paved area in sunlight, or above a central heating radiator or a toaster. The effect of hot air rising is used by balloonists. The burner heats the air enclosed by the balloon canopy to the point that it becomes sufficiently buoyant to lift the canopy, the basket, and its happy occupants.

Convection does not happen everywhere at the Earth's surface at all times, but when it does the pattern at any instant at a particular place is typically as in Figure 5.9: there are columns of rising air, with much larger regions of descending air between them. This pattern can exist on scales that at ground level range from a few centimetres across to many metres. The rising air loses energy to its surroundings, and will subsequently be displaced downwards. Don't confuse the pattern in Figure 5.9 with the drama of tornadoes. Columns of convection are so gentle that they usually go un-noticed, though glider pilots make use of them to carry the glider aloft. Glider pilots call them 'thermals'. Some birds also use thermals.

Figure 5.9 Convection transfers energy away from the Earth's surface to the atmosphere.

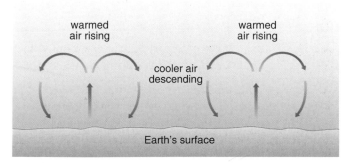

Latent heat

In addition to conveying warmed air upwards, convection plays an essential role in a quite different mechanism of energy loss by the Earth's surface. This involves the evaporation of liquid water to produce water vapour, a phenomenon you met in Section 4.1 of Block 1. Convection carries this water vapour upwards, enabling more water to evaporate from the surface. The source of this surface water is not just seas and lakes, but any moisture at the surface, such as damp soil and also vegetation. Ice can change state directly to water vapour by a process called sublimation, and this too contributes to the water vapour in the atmosphere.

But how does evaporation remove energy from the Earth's surface? Evaporation requires energy to be transferred to the liquid or ice in order to produce the vapour (for reasons that will become apparent in Section 6). This energy is called **latent heat**, the word 'latent' denoting that the heat doesn't cause a temperature change, but causes a change in state, in this case from liquid or solid, to gas (water vapour). The latent heat is extracted from the Earth's surface and so the surface tends to cool as the water evaporates. Try dampening the palm of your hand with water or perfume, and then wave it vigorously to promote evaporation — the cooling should be obvious. The evaporation of sweat in a strong wind also produces obvious cooling.

As air rises its temperature decreases. If the temperature falls low enough some of the vapour in the air condenses to form a large number of liquid droplets or icy particles — clouds. Indeed, puffy clouds often appear in rising columns of air, as Figure 5.10 shows. If it takes an input of heat to produce vapour from liquid or solid, you might expect heat to be given out in the condensation of vapour to produce liquid and solid, and indeed this is the case. The latent heat given out by condensation heats the atmosphere.

Figure 5.10 Clouds forming in rising columns of air, a consequence of water vapour carried upwards by convection. This water vapour is evaporated from the Earth's surface, which consequently loses energy via latent heat. When the water vapour condenses the latent heat is given out and raises the temperature of the atmosphere. Energy is thus transferred from the Earth's surface to the atmosphere. Precipitation from the atmosphere returns water to the ground.

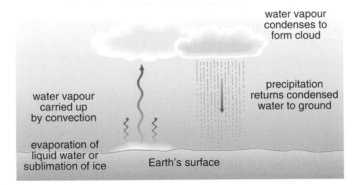

The evaporation and condensation of water thus transfers energy from the Earth's surface to the Earth's atmosphere. Ultimately, precipitation returns the condensed water to the ground, mostly as rain or snow, where it is susceptible again to evaporation or sublimation.

Question 5.4 In two or three sentences, explain why atmospheric convection helps to reduce the level of atmospheric pollution at the ground (pollution from vehicle exhausts, industrial processes, and so on). ◀

Question 5.5 If at some particular time there is no convection over some region of the Earth's surface, and no wind, explain why the surface in that region can lose little energy by way of latent heat. ◀

5.2.2 Infrared radiation emitted by the Earth's surface

Though convection is an important means by which the Earth's surface loses energy, the greatest rate of energy loss is by another process. This is the electromagnetic radiation *emitted* by the Earth's surface. This emitted radiation is *not* the same thing as the solar radiation *reflected* by the Earth's surface, which was shown in Figure

5.5c. Reflected radiation merely 'bounces' off the surface, whereas **emitted radiation** originates within the surface. What is the source of this emitted radiation?

In everyday life we see most objects by *reflected* radiation. During the day we see outdoor scenes by the visible solar radiation (sunlight) they reflect, and during the night we see indoor scenes by the light reflected from a source such as an electric light bulb. The sources of this reflected radiation are the Sun and the bulb, respectively. If we look at the glowing bulb itself we are seeing the light *emitted* by the hot wire in it: this wire is emitting light, not reflecting it from elsewhere. Likewise, were we to look directly at the Sun (please don't — it will damage your eyes!) then we would see the light emitted by the Sun.

The emitted radiation originates from the atoms that constitute the objects. (You will learn about atoms in Section 6.) Atoms are always jostling about, and one consequence of this is that they emit electromagnetic radiation. The details of this process are not relevant here: the important point is that *all* objects emit electromagnetic radiation — this includes you, the surface of the Earth and the atmosphere.

Why then can we see the emission from the bulb and the Sun, but not that from the Earth's surface? The answer is that the Sun and the bulb emit sufficient *visible* radiation for our eyes to see it, whereas the Earth's surface emits negligible amounts of visible radiation. The radiation emitted by the Earth's surface is largely of infrared wavelengths, which are not visible to the human eye. This is shown in Figure 5.11.

The curve labelled 'Earth's surface' in Figure 5.11 shows how the power in the radiation from the Earth's surface is distributed among the various wavelengths. At a particular wavelength the distance of the line from the wavelength axis is an indication of the power emitted at that wavelength — the greater the distance, the greater the power. A graph of the power of the radiation versus wavelength is called a **spectrum**.

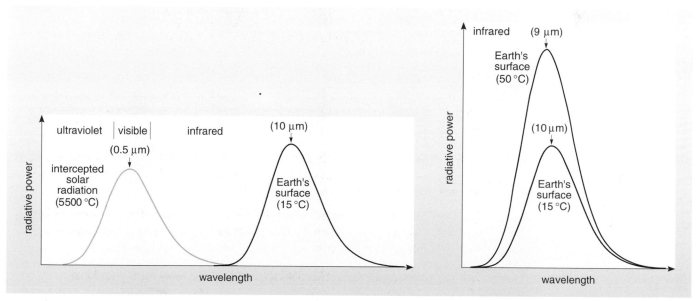

Figure 5.11   The distribution over wavelength of the power of the radiation emitted by the surface of the Earth, and of the solar radiation that the Earth intercepts. The values of the wavelengths corresponding to the peak of each spectrum are indicated. Note that the solar spectrum has been simplified.

Figure 5.12   The spectrum of the radiation emitted by the Earth's surface at a temperature of 15 °C, and at a temperature of 50 °C.

● From Figure 5.11, what subrange of electromagnetic radiation is emitted by the Earth's surface, and what subranges are absent?

○ The Earth's surface emits infrared radiation, but does not emit appreciable amounts of visible or ultraviolet radiation.

Figure 5.11 also shows the spectrum of the solar radiation intercepted by the Earth. You can see that this spectrum is dominated by shorter wavelengths, and the maximum power — the 'peak' — is at visible wavelengths.

But why are the wavelength ranges different? It all comes down to temperature. The GMST is 15 °C whereas the surface of the Sun is at the huge temperature of 5 500 °C. The higher the temperature of an object the more the spectrum of emitted radiation shifts to shorter wavelengths. This is why a metal heated to a modest temperature glows red, whereas at a higher temperature it glows yellow — yellow light has a shorter wavelength than red light (Figure 5.1).

Another property of emitted radiation that changes with temperature is its total power. Figure 5.12 compares the spectrum of the radiation emitted by the Earth's surface at its present temperature of 15 °C with the spectrum were the surface temperature to be 50 °C. You can see that, when the temperature rises, as well as a shift to shorter wavelengths there is also a general increase in the power radiated. This is an extremely important result, crucial for our understanding of the GMST, as Question 5.6 illustrates.

Question 5.6 In applying the leaky tank analogy to the GMST, we asserted that as the GMST rises, the rate of energy loss from the Earth's surface increases. In a couple of sentences, explain why Figure 5.12 supports this assertion. ◀

Finally, there is an apparently curious feature of Figures 5.11 and 5.12 that needs clearing up. In Figure 5.12 a rise in temperature from 15 °C to 50 °C produces a substantial increase in the power of the radiation, whereas in Figure 5.11 a much larger difference in temperature of 15 °C to 5 500 °C is associated with a rather slight difference in power. This is because in Figure 5.11 the solar spectrum is for the solar radiation *intercepted* by the Earth, as in Figure 5.4. This is only a tiny fraction of the power emitted by the Sun. By contrast, in Figure 5.12 the radiation in both cases is from the same object, the whole surface of the Earth.

5.3 Atmospheric radiation absorbed by the Earth's surface

You have seen that the Earth's surface is at a temperature such that most of the emitted radiation is at infrared wavelengths. Some of the emitted radiation escapes to space, but most of it is absorbed by the Earth's atmosphere. This absorbed radiation is a fourth source of energy for the atmosphere.

● What are the three sources you have already met?

○ There is absorbed solar radiation (Figure 5.7), energy transferred by convection, and latent heat given out when water vapour condenses.

The energy gains by the atmosphere sustain the atmospheric temperatures. The atmosphere is far less dense than the Earth but it still consists of matter and therefore it too *emits* radiation in accord with its temperature. Atmospheric temperatures are not hugely different from surface temperatures, and so the radiation emitted by the atmosphere is also predominantly at infrared wavelengths.

This atmospheric radiation gives rise to a second source of energy for the surface.

⬤ What is the only significant source of energy for the Earth's surface that has been described so far?

◯ This is the solar radiation absorbed by the Earth's surface (Figure 5.7).

Atmospheric radiation travels in all directions, and some of it escapes to space. The rest ultimately reaches the ground, and thus constitutes another energy gain by the surface, to add to solar radiation. However, it is important to realize that atmospheric radiation is *derived* from solar radiation. This is because all of the four energy gains by the atmosphere depend on solar radiation: the atmosphere is warmed by the Sun directly; it is also warmed indirectly by convection, latent heat, and surface emission of radiation, all of which arise from the heating of the Earth's surface by solar radiation. Therefore, the energy gain by the Earth's surface is dominated by solar radiation, be this direct or indirect.

Figure 5.13 brings together the various processes that we have considered in this section and in Section 5.2. As in Figure 5.7, the width of each arrow is proportional to the rate of energy transfer. The upward pointing arrow at the left of the figure represents the rate at which energy is transferred from the Earth's surface to the atmosphere through convection plus latent heat. The arrow at the right leaving the Earth's surface represents the rate at which infrared radiation is emitted by the Earth's surface. This arrow splits into two, a thin arrow representing the small amount of emitted radiation that escapes to space, and the thicker arrow that curves over and ends in the atmosphere.

⬤ What does this curved arrow represent?

◯ It represents the rate at which radiation emitted by the Earth's surface is absorbed by the atmosphere.

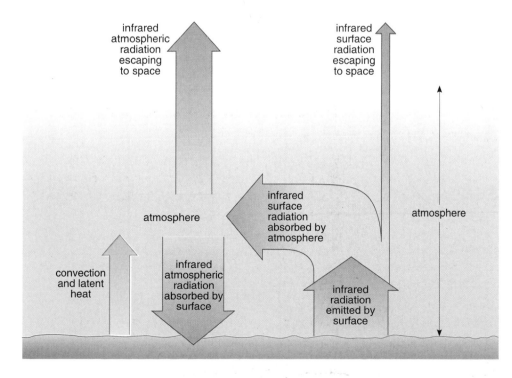

Figure 5.13 The exchanges of infrared radiation involving the Earth's surface and atmosphere. Also included are the convective and latent heat transfers. The width of each arrow is proportional to the rate of energy transfer. Values are added in Figure 5.14.

The central arrows originate in the atmosphere, and represent the infrared radiation emitted by the atmosphere. The upward pointing arrow represents the amount of this infrared radiation that escapes to space, and the downward pointing arrow represents the amount that is absorbed by the Earth's surface. Note that even though the arrows starting and stopping in the atmosphere do so in a small region in the centre of Figure 5.13, the atmospheric energy gains and losses take place throughout the atmosphere.

We have now met all of the important energy gains and losses at the Earth's surface. The time has come to put them all together and obtain an overview, so that we can see the processes that determine the GMST.

5.4 So, what determines the GMST?

5.4.1 An overview of energy gains and losses

Figure 5.14 is what we have been working towards: a diagram giving an overview of the rates of energy gain and loss by the Earth's surface and atmosphere. The component parts of this diagram are Figures 5.7 and 5.13, which have already been discussed, but this synthesis will now be explored in some detail.

Figure 5.14 Rates of energy gain and loss by the Earth's surface and atmosphere. Note that even though the arrows starting and stopping in the atmosphere do so in a small region in the centre, the atmospheric energy gains and losses that they represent take place throughout the atmosphere. 100 units represent the rate at which solar radiation is intercepted by the Earth. The width of each arrow is proportional to the rate of energy transfer.

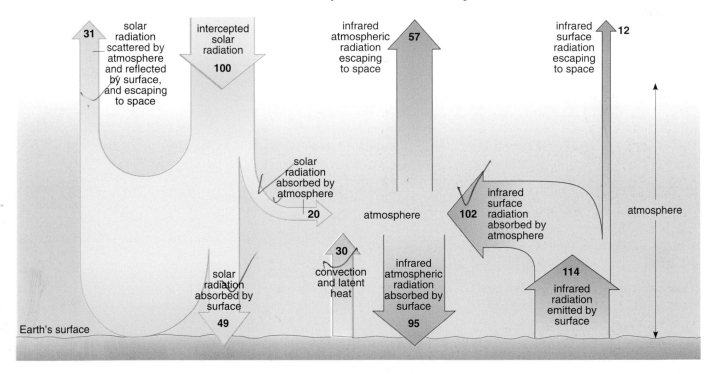

The left-hand side of Figure 5.14 is the same as Figure 5.7: it shows the rates of energy gain and loss by the Earth's surface and atmosphere that involve solar radiation *directly*. Remember that 100 units represent the rate at which solar electromagnetic radiation is intercepted by the Earth: of these 100 units, 49 units are absorbed by the surface and 20 units by the atmosphere, and the rest (31 units) escapes back to space.

The central part of Figure 5.14 (coloured green) shows the rate of energy transfer from the Earth's surface to the atmosphere by a combination of convection and latent heat. There are 30 units transferred in this way, and it is a loss from the surface.

The right-hand side of Figure 5.14 is exactly the same as Figure 5.13 and involves the infrared radiation described in Section 5.3, but now values have been added to the arrows. If we start at the extreme right, then we see that 114 units are emitted by the Earth's surface, with 12 of the 114 units escaping to space, and the rest, the major part, 102 units, being absorbed by the atmosphere. The atmosphere emits infrared radiation at a rate of 152 units. Of this, 57 units escape to space, and the remaining 95 units are absorbed by the surface.

At this point, a question might spring to mind: if the Earth intercepts solar radiation at the rate of 100 units, how can 114 units be emitted by the Earth's surface, and 152 units be emitted by the atmosphere? Tackling the following question should help you understand this apparent paradox.

Question 5.7   (a) From Figure 5.14 calculate the difference between the rate of energy gain and the rate of energy loss for:

(i) the Earth as a whole (consider the solar radiation intercepted by the Earth, and the radiation returning or escaping to space from the atmosphere and the surface);

(ii) the Earth's surface;

(iii) the Earth's atmosphere.

(b) From your calculations in part (a), what do you conclude about the GMST? ◀

The answer to Question 5.7a(i) shows that there is no net energy gain or loss by the Earth, and the answers to the rest of Question 5.7a show that this is also the case separately for the surface and the atmosphere. Everything is in a dynamic steady state: in spite of all those energy flows there is no net accumulation of energy in any part of the system, and no net loss. It is perhaps now less puzzling that some of the rates of energy exchange in Figure 5.14 exceed the rate at which solar energy is intercepted by the Earth. The rates of energy exchange between different parts of a system in a steady state can be as high as you like, as long as the rate of energy gain by each part equals the rate of energy loss by the same part, so the net energy transfer is zero. In other words, the rates of circulation of energy *within* a system can be greater than the rate of flow into and out of a system. In a rather extreme analogy, there's a good deal of blood flow inside you, but (we hope) a negligible flow of blood out or in.

If you are still puzzled by the high rates of energy exchange between the surface and the atmosphere then it might help to return to a water-based analogy. In Figure 5.15 the flow from the tap is the analogy of the solar radiation intercepted by the Earth, and the flow from the base of the lower tank is the analogy of all of the radiation returning or escaping from the Earth to space. Each of these two water flow rates represents energy transfer at a rate of 100 units. It would be possible to represent the rest of Figure 5.14 in the form of a water analogy, but this would give us a plumber's nightmare assemblage of tanks, pipes and pumps. Fortunately the much simpler plumbing in Figure 5.15 suffices to illustrate the general notion that there can be higher rates of internal circulation than the rates of flow in and out. Thus, water is leaking from the upper to the lower tank at a rate of 300 units, and, to maintain a steady state, water is being pumped from the lower to the upper tank at a rate of 200 units. Note that, just as the Sun is the source of all the energy flow rates in Figure 5.14, so the tap is the source of all the water flow rates in Figure 5.15.

Figure 5.15 A water analogy to illustrate that the rate of flow within a system can exceed the rate of flow into and out of a system.

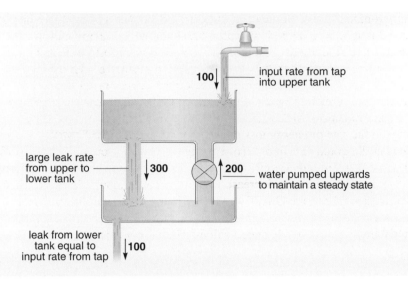

input rate from tap into upper tank

100

large leak rate from upper to lower tank

300

200 water pumped upwards to maintain a steady state

leak from lower tank equal to input rate from tap

100

Activity 5.2   Alternative diagram of the rates of energy gain and loss by the Earth's surface and atmosphere

This activity will reinforce your understanding of Figure 5.14 by getting you to label a different form of the diagram. ◀

5.4.2   Why the GMST has a particular value

In broad terms, we can see from Figure 5.14 that the value of the GMST depends on:

- the rate at which the Earth intercepts solar radiation: this rate is obtained by multiplying the area over which radiation is intercepted (the grey disc in Figure 5.4) by the solar constant;

- the properties of the atmosphere, particularly those that influence:

  the scattering and absorption of solar radiation;

  the absorption of the radiation emitted by the Earth's surface (which is at infrared wavelengths);

  the emission of radiation by the atmosphere (also at infrared wavelengths);

  the rate of energy transfer via convection and latent heat;

- the properties of the Earth's surface, particularly those that influence:

  the reflection and absorption of solar radiation;

  the emission of radiation by the surface (which is at infrared wavelengths);

  the availability of water for evaporation.

If any of these factors is changed, then the GMST will change, unless, in changing several things at once, there is overall compensation in which case there is no net effect on the GMST.

Let's examine the case of the solar constant, and perform a 'thought experiment'. Suppose that initially there is a steady state with the Sun shining as it is today, when suddenly, as in the top graph in Figure 5.16, the solar constant increases to a slightly higher value, with no change in atmospheric and surface properties. What would happen? At once, the Earth's surface would receive more solar radiation than before, and because the surface would absorb the same *fraction*, it would therefore absorb more solar radiation. At the instant that the solar constant changed there would be no change in the rate of energy loss by the surface, so the GMST would start to rise, as in the middle graph in Figure 5.16. This rise in GMST would cause the surface to emit more infrared radiation (Figure 5.12) and so the rate of energy loss would increase as the temperature increased, as in the bottom graph in Figure 5.16. If there were no atmosphere, the GMST would continue to rise until the rate at which energy was lost by the surface equalled the new rate of energy gain by the surface. There would then be a new steady state, with the GMST higher than before.

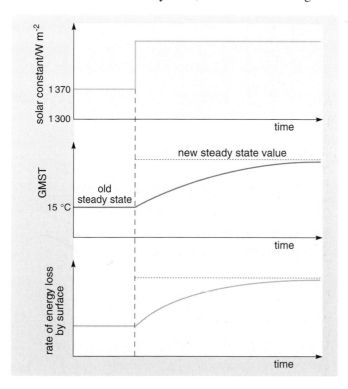

Figure 5.16   The response of the GMST to an increase in the solar constant, and the consequent increase in the rate of energy loss from the Earth's surface. Note that the solar constant axis does not start at zero, so the solar constant is increased only slightly.

The presence of an atmosphere makes things more complicated, because the surface also receives infrared radiation from the atmosphere, and loses energy through convection and latent heat. But the outcome would be similar, that an increase in the solar constant would cause an increase in GMST.

The solar constant does indeed vary! Recall that the value we quoted earlier is an average value over several years. If we compare these averages then it is found that the solar constant varies by about 0.1% over a decade or so, and by rather more in the longer term. The steady state in Figure 5.14 is therefore slightly disturbed in reality, and as a consequence the GMST does vary. Variations in the solar constant have been a contributory factor to the past variations in the GMST that you met in Sections 2 and 3. But there is a host of other ways of disturbing the steady state. To conclude this section we will consider just one more — the effect on the GMST of changing the rate at which the atmosphere absorbs and emits infrared radiation: this brings us to the much publicized greenhouse effect.

5.4.3 The greenhouse effect

In order to discuss the greenhouse effect, it is convenient to distinguish in Figure 5.11 between the radiation emitted by the Earth's surface and the radiation emitted by the Sun.

⬤ Which radiation is characterized by longer wavelengths?

◯ The radiation from the Earth's surface.

Moreover, the radiation from the Earth's surface is confined to the longer wavelength part of the infrared region of the spectrum, whereas the solar radiation in the infrared region is at shorter wavelengths. Consequently, the radiation from the Earth's surface is often called *longwave* infrared radiation. The atmosphere also emits longwave infrared radiation.

⬤ From Figure 5.14, write down the fraction of the radiation emitted by the Earth's surface that is absorbed by the atmosphere. Express the fraction in decimal form, and as a percentage.

◯ The fraction is $\frac{102}{114} = 0.89$. As a percentage this is $0.89 \times 100\% = 89\%$.

Thus, most of the radiation emitted by the Earth's surface is absorbed by the atmosphere. By contrast, only 20% of the incoming solar radiation is absorbed. The fractions (or percentages) absorbed are called the absorptivities.

Suppose that, somehow, the atmospheric properties were suddenly adjusted so that the *only* change was a reduction in longwave infrared absorptivity: suppose that all other atmospheric properties, the solar constant, and all the surface properties remain the same. The atmosphere would therefore absorb a smaller proportion of the infrared radiation emitted by the surface. In Figure 5.14 the 114 units of energy emitted by the Earth's surface would no longer divide into 102 units absorbed by the atmosphere and 12 units escaping to space. The amount absorbed by the atmosphere would be less than 102 units and the amount escaping to space would be correspondingly more. It turns out that the atmosphere would then *emit* less infrared radiation. This means that there would be less radiation for the Earth's surface to absorb: it would absorb less than the 95 units in Figure 5.14. Nothing else has changed at the surface, so the Earth's surface would be losing energy faster than it would be gaining it.

⬤ So, what would happen to the surface temperature?

◯ It would fall — the surface would cool.

The cooling would not, however, continue indefinitely. The cooler the surface, the lower the rate at which it emits radiation. (It is also possible that the rate of energy loss via convection and latent heat would fall.) The cooling of the surface thus continues until the rate of energy loss by the surface equals the new, lower rate of gain. A new steady state is then in place, with the surface at a new, lower temperature, as in Figure 5.17.

To reinforce this conclusion let's return to the original water tank analogy in Figure 4.3, in which the flow of water from the tap represents the rate of energy gain by the Earth's surface, and thus includes the infrared radiation emitted by the atmosphere. By reducing atmospheric radiation we have turned the tap down a bit: the leak rate then exceeds the rate of supply, so the water level falls until the leak rate has declined to the point where it again equals the new supply rate, as in Figure 4.3c.

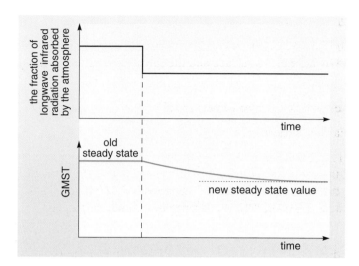

Figure 5.17 The change in the GMST when the atmospheric absorptivity of longwave infrared radiation is reduced, with all else remaining the same.

For the Earth today, if there were no radiation emitted by the atmosphere, and if all else stayed the same, the GMST would be about twenty degrees below 0 °C. Life as we know it would not exist on Earth, and perhaps there would be no life here at all. Our atmosphere thus acts as a powerful 'radiation trap', and the GMST is considerably higher as a consequence.

> The rise in surface temperature that results from the radiation emitted by the atmosphere is called the **greenhouse effect**.

Box 5.2, *Greenhouses and the greenhouse effect*, explains why it has this name, though the explanation is not essential for our story.

Box 5.2 Greenhouses and the greenhouse effect

The greenhouse effect gets its name from the higher temperature in an unheated greenhouse than in the air outside. Much of this difference is nothing to do with the greenhouse effect, but arises from the containment of warm air that would otherwise convect upwards and be replaced by cooler air. A small part of the difference is because the glass panes in a greenhouse behave towards radiation rather like the Earth's atmosphere (Figure 5.18). The panes absorb a large fraction of the longwave infrared radiation emitted by the plants, soil and other surfaces within the greenhouse. Radiation emitted by the panes then makes a small contribution to the rise in temperature in the greenhouse.

The high transparency of glass to solar radiation is obvious from our ability to see through it so well. Therefore little solar radiation is absorbed. But what about the longwave infrared absorption? If you have a glass jug (*not* plastic or metal) and an electric cooker you can demonstrate that the longwave infrared absorption of glass is high, as follows.

Switch on a hot-plate but do not let it get so hot that it glows. It is then emitting predominantly longwave infrared radiation. Place your hand to one side of the hot-plate (not too near!) so that you can feel the warmth: your skin has infrared sensors. Do not place your hand above the hot-plate or you will also be receiving energy by convection. Take the glass jug and cover your hand with it,

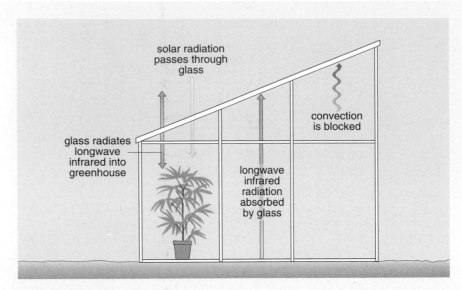

Figure 5.18 How a greenhouse can be warmer than the surrounding air.

but not too near the hot-plate or the jug might crack. You should at once experience a loss of warming in your hand. The sensation of warmth is restored when the jug is removed. This shows that glass blocks longwave infrared radiation. You cannot tell whether the radiation is being absorbed or reflected. In fact some is reflected but the greater part is absorbed.

For the Earth, the fact that the GMST is considerably higher than it would be if the atmosphere allowed longwave infrared radiation to escape to space shows that the greenhouse effect is not a 'bad thing': indeed, it is a 'good thing'! It is *changes* in the greenhouse effect that could have undesirable consequences for us. The greenhouse effect depends on atmospheric gases that strongly absorb longwave infrared radiation. These are called **greenhouse gases**. The greater the amount of a greenhouse gas in the atmosphere, the higher the GMST (if everything else stays the same). We clearly need to look more closely at the Earth's atmosphere to identify the greenhouse gases, and also to gain a deeper understanding of the other atmospheric properties that influence the GMST. This is a major task for Section 6.

Activity 5.3 Energy balance diagram for the Moon

This activity will reinforce your understanding of the energy balance diagram of the Earth, shown in Figure 5.14, by applying the underlying concepts to a different object — the Moon. ◀

5.5 Summary of Section 5

Most of the solar radiation reaching the Earth is in the form of light, but some is ultraviolet radiation and some is infrared radiation. Gamma-rays, X-rays, ultraviolet radiation, light, infrared radiation, microwaves and radio waves are all forms of electromagnetic radiation, with different wavelengths. They travel through space with the same speed, the speed of light, transferring energy from one place to another.

Figure 5.14 summarizes the various ways in which the Earth's surface and atmosphere gain and lose energy.

The Earth's surface gains energy by absorbing a large fraction of the intercepted solar radiation, and by absorbing most of the infrared radiation emitted by the atmosphere.

The Earth's surface loses energy through convection in the atmosphere, and through the evaporation of water at the surface (latent heat transfer). It also loses energy through the emission of infrared radiation. This has a much longer wavelength than visible radiation, and is called longwave infrared radiation.

Most of the longwave infrared radiation emitted by the surface is absorbed by the atmosphere. This, plus the convective and latent heat transfers, sustains the atmospheric temperature, and therefore sustains the rate at which the atmosphere emits infrared radiation.

In the steady state, the rate of energy gain by the Earth's surface equals the rate of loss, and therefore the global mean surface temperature (GMST) is not changing.

The Earth's GMST is determined by the solar constant, and by various properties of the Earth's surface and atmosphere.

The GMST is raised considerably because of the greenhouse effect. This effect depends on atmospheric gases that absorb most of the longwave infrared radiation emitted by the Earth's surface.

Activity 5.4   Review of progress

This activity gives you the opportunity to review your progress, and thus links to Activity 1.1. This would also be a good point for you to re-read Section 1.1 to see where you are in the story of Block 2, and what still remains. ◄

6 The Earth's atmosphere

You have seen that the GMST depends on the energy balance at the surface of the Earth. The ultimate source of the energy is the Sun, but solar radiation is not simply absorbed by the Earth's surface, and the radiation emitted by the surface does not simply escape to space. On the contrary, the presence of an atmosphere has a profound effect on the surface energy balance that determines the GMST. In brief, the atmosphere

- reduces the amount of solar radiation that reaches the surface;
- absorbs some of the infrared radiation emitted by the surface;
- emits infrared radiation, some of which is absorbed by the surface;
- makes possible the loss of energy from the surface via convection and latent heat transfer.

To appreciate the factors that control these processes requires an understanding of the structure and composition of the atmosphere. This is the main task for this section, but it is not the only one. Our examination of the atmosphere also provides the opportunity to introduce some basic science that you will need in subsequent sections.

As you will see, the atmosphere consists largely of a mixture of gases. In Section 6.1 we start by examining exactly what is meant by the term 'gas', and then introduce a model that explains and predicts some of the properties of a gas. We apply this model to the atmosphere in Section 6.2. This helps us to understand the structure of the atmosphere and the way in which energy is exchanged with the Earth's surface. In Sections 6.3 and 6.4 we look more closely at atmospheric gases and their properties in order to understand the behaviour of the atmosphere. In Section 6.5 we identify which gases are responsible for the greenhouse effect.

6.1 What is a gas?

We can see that solids, such as rocks, and liquids, such as water, have substance — but what of the air? On the one hand we are told we are surrounded by air, and you may even be aware of some of its properties, but on the other hand personal experience seems to suggest there is nothing there — we cannot see or touch it. This is not a new problem. Until the 17th century there was no real concept of a gas, as William H. Brock describes:

> But perhaps the greatest stumbling block to the further development of chemistry was a case of insufficient analysis — there was a complete absence of a knowledge or concept of the gaseous state of matter. Chemistry remained a two-dimensional science, which studied, and only had equipment and apparatus to handle, solids and liquids.

> (W. H. Brock, *The Fontana History of Chemistry*, Fontana Press, 1992, p. 42)

It wasn't really until late in the 18th century that a third state of matter was recognized, as the following quote from the French chemist Antoine-Laurent Lavoisier (1743–1794) shows:

> All bodies in nature present themselves to us in three different states. Some are solid like stones, earth, salts and metals. Others are fluid like water,

mercury, spirits of wine; and others finally are in a third state which I shall
call the state of expansion or of vapours, such as water when one heats it
above the boiling point.

However, just what he meant by a 'state of expansion or of vapours' is not obvious.

Activity 6.1 *Composition and properties of air*

You will already have some knowledge about the composition and properties of air.
In this activity, you will summarize what you know, and note down any relevant
questions that you may have. At the end of Section 6.5, you will be able to repeat this
exercise to see how your knowledge has developed. ◀

You were introduced to gases in Block 1, using the same example as Lavoisier's —
water vapour. When we boil a kettle some of the liquid water is transformed into a
gas. If this comes into contact with a cold surface it condenses back into liquid water.
This suggests that although it is invisible, a gas has substance, because liquid water
has been transferred from the kettle to the cold surface. You also learnt that a gas will
flow and take the shape of its container. However, unlike a liquid, a gas will fill its
container completely — it does not have a fixed volume. One of the aims of this
section is to revisit some of these ideas and develop a model that makes sense of
these properties.

Activity 6.2 *Evidence that air has substance*

This activity involves you watching a series of video clips and deciding which of
them provides evidence that supports the hypothesis that air has substance. ◀

Some of the demonstrations in Activity 6.2 clearly showed that the air *does* have
substance; some of them did not confirm that air has substance, but none of them
disproved the hypothesis. In a situation like this, where we have some evidence in
favour and none to the contrary, it is scientific practice to proceed on the assumption
that our hypothesis is correct. Of course, if contradictory evidence were discovered
we would need to modify our hypothesis to accommodate the new evidence, or
abandon it in favour of a new hypothesis consistent with all the evidence. Over the
years there has been a great deal of evidence to suggest that air has substance and
nothing to contradict this; thus the hypothesis has stood the test of time.

So far, we have been rather loose with the phrase 'has substance'; we have used it to
infer that there is something there, that air has mass and can move other objects, but
this description is still rather woolly. To help us make sense of gases we shall develop
a model that describes the structure of solids, liquids, and gases. The model is a
scientific one, and like all scientific models it is a simplified representation of the real
world. Scientific models aid understanding by focusing on some particular aspect(s)
of reality. We shall present no real evidence for the model of solids, liquids, and
gases, but will use it as a framework to explain the various properties of gases,
including those shown in the demonstrations on the video 'Does the air have
substance?'. We shall show that the real strength of the model is that it explains these
properties, and also helps us to predict other properties.

In Block 1, Section 6.1.3, you saw that water is made up of small particles. If a
raindrop is halved about 67 times, we are left not with a drop of water as we know it
but with a single particle of water, called a water molecule. If this were then halved
we would no longer have water. In fact all matter is made up of a large number of
very, very small particles — far too small to see — and very different from, and very
much smaller than, other more familiar types of particle, such as the specks of dust or

pollen that you can sometimes see moving around in the air in a shaft of light. In this section, from now on, we shall restrict the use of the term 'particle' to mean the smallest characteristic entity of a particular substance. For water, this smallest entity is a water molecule. Just what is meant by a 'water molecule' is taken up in Section 6.3, where you will also learn more about the particles that make up other substances. For the moment, it is sufficient to think of these particles as tiny hard spheres: these spheres are the basic feature of the simple **particle model**.

One of the key properties of the particles of which matter is made is that they are attracted to each other, but this attraction decreases the farther apart the particles are. In the **solid state**, the particles are packed closely such that their mutual attraction holds them tightly together. As a result the particles have fixed positions relative to each other, as shown in Figure 6.1a; the particles do not swap places, but they do 'vibrate' about their fixed positons, as indicated in Figure 6.1a for a few of them. In the **liquid state**, the particles are still close enough to be attracted to each other, but they are not arranged in a regular way (Figure 6.1b). The particles move around, jostling and swapping positions. In the **gaseous state**, the particles are much farther apart (Figure 6.1c), so much so that there is little attraction between them. In this state the particles are moving around rapidly in a random, chaotic manner, frequently colliding with, and bouncing off, each other and the walls of the container.

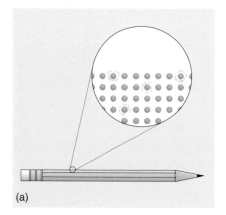

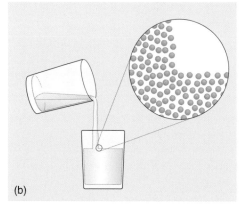

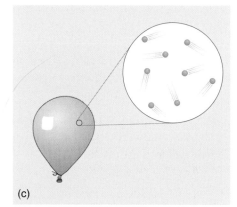

(a) (b) (c)

Figure 6.1 The arrangement of particles in the (a) solid, (b) liquid and (c) gaseous states.

One of the properties of a solid is that it keeps its shape irrespective of the shape of its container — that is, it does not flow. Our particle model is in agreement with this; in solids the particles occupy fixed positions relative to each other, and do not swap positions, and so the solid cannot change shape (unless large external forces are applied).

⬤ Does a liquid keep its shape?

◯ No, a liquid flows; it takes up the shape of the vessel it is in. (At a fixed temperature it does have a fixed volume.)

Our particle model of a liquid reflects these properties. In a liquid the particles can move relative to each other, so a liquid can take up any shape. Nevertheless, the particles are still held close together, effectively giving a very, very big assembly of particles. So whatever the final shape of the liquid, the overall volume remains constant. The particles behave rather like the tiny polystyrene spheres that are used to stuff bean bags and the like. The bag can take up all kinds of shapes but its volume remains the same.

A gas, on the other hand, not only flows but will fill its container completely whatever the volume. Here the particles are moving around in all directions and so will spread out until they meet some kind of barrier — the walls of the container. Notice that we have to be careful with our language here; when we say a gas fills its container, we do not mean that in some way the particles swell up or increase in number to fill the available space. We have the same number of particles, but they are spread farther apart.

Block 1 used water as an example of a material that can exist in different states, but it should be remembered that, depending on the conditions, *any* substance can exist as a solid, a liquid or a gas. For example, a solid iron bar will melt to give liquid iron when the temperature reaches 1 535 °C. If we heat it further, its temperature rises and it boils to give iron as a gas at 3 027 °C. We can explain these changes of state with our model. When a solid melts, the ordered positioning of the particles starts to break down. **Melting** occurs at a particular temperature, known as the melting temperature, and involves the transition from a state where the particles don't swap positions, to one where they do. This transition requires an input of energy so that the particles have enough energy to move from their fixed positions. Thus to melt a solid at its melting temperature we need to put energy into the material. This is called the latent heat of melting.

Freezing is the opposite process to melting — a liquid changes into a solid.

⬤ Explain what happens during freezing, using our particle model.

◯ Freezing of a liquid involves the transition from a state in which the particles can swap positions, the liquid state, to one in which the particles occupy specific positions, the solid state.

Whereas energy has to be supplied in order to melt a solid, the reverse of this process, freezing, involves giving out energy. In fact, for a given mass of material, exactly the same amount of energy is released when a liquid freezes as was required to convert the solid into a liquid in the first place.

As you saw in Block 1, the change from a liquid to a gas is known as evaporation and involves a transition from a state in which the particles are close together to one in which they are much farther apart. In this transition, energy needs to be supplied to overcome the mutual attraction between the particles and cause them to spread apart. Thus we need to provide energy to convert a substance from a liquid into a gas, as we saw in Section 5.2.1. This energy is called the latent heat of vaporization. It was noted in Section 5.2.1 that this is why our skin cools when water evaporates from it — our skin supplies the energy for the water to evaporate and so is cooled down.

Evaporation usually occurs from the surface of a liquid, as shown in Figure 6.2. It can occur at any temperature. However, the ease with which particles move from the liquid to the gaseous state increases as the temperature increases. This is one of the reasons why washing dries quickly on a hot summer day. The highest temperature at which the transition from liquid to gas can take place is called the boiling temperature. At this temperature the conversion of a liquid into a gas occurs so readily that gas bubbles form in the liquid, which is how we recognize boiling. At higher temperatures the substance is completely gaseous.

As you also saw in Book 1, condensation involves a transition from the gaseous state to the liquid state.

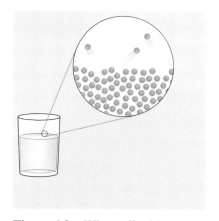

Figure 6.2 When a liquid evaporates particles leave the surface of the liquid.

○ Describe the process of condensation at the particle level.

○ Condensation involves the transition from a state in which the particles are far away from, and effectively independent of each other, to a state in which the particles are closer together and attraction between particles is larger.

For evaporation to occur, an input of energy is needed to work against the mutual attraction between the particles and spread them out. The reverse process, condensation, involves the particles coming together. This process gives out energy, and so when a gas condenses to a liquid energy is released.

You may have been wondering what causes the particles in a gas to move in all directions and what affects their speed. The key factor here is the temperature. At the particle level, temperature is a measure of the energy of the random motions of the particles: the greater the temperature, the greater the energy of motion and the greater the speed of the particles. If a solid, or a liquid, or a gas is heated, then at the particle level the energy of random motion increases, and we see this as a rise in temperature. Thus, as we heat a solid the constituent particles vibrate more energetically about their fixed positions. Eventually the particles are vibrating so violently that they can leave their fixed positions — the solid melts to give a liquid. As this liquid is heated, the particles in the liquid move around more quickly. At the boiling temperature these particles are moving so fast that they can easily free themselves from each other and the liquid is completely converted into a gas. Further heating of the gas causes the particles to move around more quickly. If the gas is in a container, its volume is fixed, and heating leads to a build-up of pressure in the container, as described in Box 6.1, *Under pressure*. This is why you should never throw aerosol cans on a fire!

Box 6.1 *Under pressure*

When we pump up a bicycle tyre we increase the amount of gas that is inside the inner tube, that is we put in more particles. These particles are moving around and colliding with the walls of the inner tube. As we put in more particles we get more collisions; this has the effect of pushing the walls outwards. Eventually we put in so many particles that their collisions with the walls of the inner tube hold the walls firmly in place such that, inside the tyre, they provide a cushion of air for us to ride on.

Let's look at this in a little more detail. Figure 6.3 shows a number of particles colliding with a surface, such as the wall of an inner tube. The particles are moving in all directions in a chaotic fashion and bouncing off the walls of the tube. Each time a particle hits the wall it exerts a force on the wall of the tube. We experience this type of force when a ball bounces off a bat or racquet. There are so many particles in an inner tube that there is a continuous shower of particles bombarding the walls leading to a steady force, which holds the tube in shape. We say the tube is 'under pressure', or that the gas 'exerts a pressure'. In scientific terms, the **pressure** on the small section of the wall shown in Figure 6.3 is defined as the force

acting on this section divided by the surface area of this section of the wall:

$$\text{pressure} = \frac{\text{force on the surface}}{\text{area of the surface}} \qquad (6.1)$$

It is important to note that the pressure is the same throughout the inner tube.

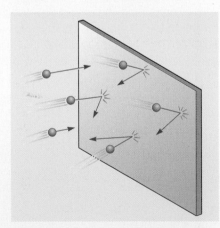

Figure 6.3 A gas exerts a force on a surface, such as the wall of an inner tube, as a result of collisions.

Force is another word (like energy and power) that is commonly used in a number of ways: 'I had to force myself to get out of bed this morning'; 'my sister is in the police force'. In science, force has a specific meaning, which you will meet in more detail in Block 3. For now all you need to know about a force is that, when it is applied to an object, it tends to cause the object to move. If, like the walls of the inner tube, the object doesn't move, it is because there is an equal and opposite force balancing out the initial force. In the case of the bicycle tyre the opposing force arises from the stretching of the rubber inner tube.

There are many units that are used to express pressure. You may have come across 'pounds per square inch', or p.s.i., which is used to measure car tyre pressures; a typical car tyre pressure would be about 30 p.s.i. Many garage air pumps also quote the pressure in another unit, the bar: a pressure of 30 p.s.i. is equivalent to about 2 bars. The **bar** is the unit of pressure that we shall use in this block.

As you might expect, if we increase the number of particles in a specific volume then, in any time interval, there will be more collisions with the walls of the container. Thus the force on the walls will increase, which in turn means an increase in the pressure. The pressure also depends on the temperature: for a gas contained in a fixed volume, the higher the temperature, the higher the pressure. As we increase the temperature, we do not increase the number of particles in a specific volume, so why does the pressure increase?

As well as the number of particles present, the pressure also depends on how often and how hard the particles hit the walls. This depends on how fast they are travelling, and temperature is a measure of this. As we heat up a gas, the particles of the gas will, on average, move more quickly. This means the force from their impact with the walls will be greater, and the particles will also collide with the walls more often. Both these factors lead to an increase in the overall force on the walls of the container. This means the pressure increases.

Activity 6.3 Active reading

In Block 1 you were introduced to the processes of active reading — highlighting or underlining key words and phrases and making notes as you are reading. We hope you have continued this practice through Block 2. This activity introduces you to a new technique, which you can apply to Box 6.1. ◀

Activity 6.4 The particle model

In this activity you will study a video that reviews the particle model of solids, liquids and gases using animations. ◀

Question 6.1   In the particle model of a gas, what is in the space between the particles? ◀

Question 6.2   (a) If we have two samples of a gas that are identical except that sample A is at a higher temperature than sample B, how do they differ at the particle level?

(b) If we mix these two samples of gas together, suggest what might happen at the particle level. ◀

Question 6.3   The air around us is a gas, so what will happen to the air if we cool it down sufficiently? ◀

6.2 What is the Earth's atmosphere?

Now that you have some familiarity with gases, we can start to make sense of the atmosphere, which in turn will help you to understand some of the factors that affect the GMST. The Earth is surrounded by a gas that we call the air. The complete layer of air is known as the **atmosphere**. It can be divided into zones, as shown in Figure 6.4. The lower atmosphere is known as the troposphere. This is the region in which we live and it is also the region where weather systems operate. Above this is the stratosphere, and higher still are other regions not shown in Figure 6.4.

Figure 6.4 Cross-section of the Earth and its atmosphere, showing the different zones with approximate altitudes (heights above sea-level).

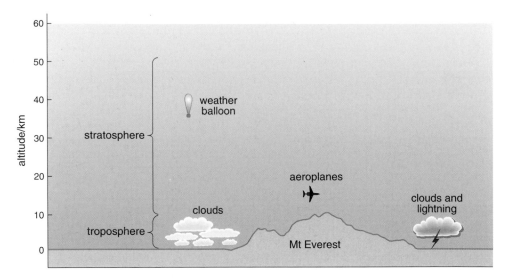

Earlier we said that a gas will expand to fill its container: that is the particles will spread throughout the available volume. The atmosphere is not held in a container, so why doesn't it just spread out into space and disappear from the surface of the Earth? The answer has to do with gravity. Just as an apple will fall to the ground under the influence of gravity, so the gas particles in the atmosphere are attracted to the Earth. If the particles were stationary they would fall straight down to the surface of the Earth to form a thin dense layer. However, because they are jostling around we get a 'shell' of gas particles around the Earth. The number of particles in a given volume (such as a cubic metre) is greatest at the surface of the Earth and decreases as we move away from the surface. This decrease is shown in Table 6.1, and schematically in Figure 6.4, where the thinning of the blue tint of the atmosphere represents the decrease in particle numbers. Like any other gas the air exerts a pressure, which depends on the number of particles in a given volume and on the temperature. The air pressure at different altitudes is also shown in Table 6.1.

Table 6.1 The number of particles in a cubic metre of air, and the air pressure, at different altitudes.

Altitude/km	Number of particles in a cubic metre of air	Air pressure/bar
0 (sea-level)	2.6×10^{25}	1.0
1 (top of Snowdon)	2.2×10^{25}	8.9×10^{-1}
10 (top of Everest)	8.7×10^{24}	2.8×10^{-1}
40	8.9×10^{22}	3.2×10^{-3}
80	5.2×10^{20}	1.3×10^{-5}
120	1.2×10^{18}	4.6×10^{-8}
160	3.8×10^{16}	2.7×10^{-9}

Some of the numbers in Table 6.1 are very large and some are very small. When (as in Question 6.6) you perform calculations involving such powers of ten you will need to use the rules discussed in Box 6.2, *Calculations involving powers of ten*.

Box 6.2 Calculations involving powers of ten

You were introduced to the use of powers of ten for large and small numbers in Block 1, but so far you have not been asked to do any calculations using them.

Suppose we have two numbers expressed in scientific notation, say 3×10^2 and 2×10^2. How do we add, subtract, multiply or divide these numbers?

Boxes 6.1 and 6.2 in Block 1 taught you how to enter powers of ten into your calculator, using the EE key (or the E or EXP key). Thus, an obvious way of carrying out these calculations is to use a calculator. To add 3×10^2 and 2×10^2 you simply use the plus key:

$$\boxed{3}\boxed{EE}\boxed{2}\boxed{+}\boxed{2}\boxed{EE}\boxed{2}\boxed{=}$$

Most calculators will display 5.0 ^{02}, which is the calculator's version of 5×10^2. In this case it might even display 500, though if the power of 10 is much larger than two, then you will not get this form of display.

Subtraction, multiplication and division are carried out similarly:

$$\boxed{3}\boxed{EE}\boxed{2}\boxed{-}\boxed{2}\boxed{EE}\boxed{2}\boxed{=} \quad 1.0 ^{02}, \text{ i.e. } 1 \times 10^2 \text{ or } 100$$

$$\boxed{3}\boxed{EE}\boxed{2}\boxed{\times}\boxed{2}\boxed{EE}\boxed{2}\boxed{=} \quad 6.0 ^{04}, \text{ i.e. } 6 \times 10^4 \text{ or } 60\,000$$

$$\boxed{3}\boxed{EE}\boxed{2}\boxed{\div}\boxed{2}\boxed{EE}\boxed{2}\boxed{=} \quad 1.5 ^{00}, \text{ i.e. } 1.5 \times 10^0 \text{ or } 1.5$$

However, rather than merely using the calculator as a 'black box' to work out these answers, it is important that you know how to perform such calculations. You will then be able to spot any silly mistakes you may make using your calculator.

If we write 3×10^2 and 2×10^2 in a more familiar fashion we have 300 and 200. Then $300 + 200 = 500 = 5 \times 10^2$. Thus, making use of the BODMAS rules in Block 1 Section 2.3, we can write $(3 \times 10^2) + (2 \times 10^2) = 5 \times 10^2$.

This agrees with a universal rule that *providing the powers of ten are the same* (in this case the power is two) then the numbers accompanying the powers of ten can simply be added:

$$(3 \times 10^2) + (2 \times 10^2) = (3 + 2) \times 10^2 = 5 \times 10^2$$

Similarly with subtraction: providing the powers of ten are the same, then the numbers accompanying the powers of ten can simply be subtracted.

● What is $(3 \times 10^2) - (2 \times 10^2)$?

○ $(3 \times 10^2) - (2 \times 10^2) = (3 - 2) \times 10^2 = 1 \times 10^2$.

This is what we would expect, since $300 - 200 = 100$.

But what do we do if the two numbers we want to add or subtract are *not* raised to the same power of ten, for example $(2.0 \times 10^3) + (3.0 \times 10^2)$?

To add or subtract two numbers with powers of ten we need to write them so that they are both raised to the same power of ten, and then we add or subtract the numbers accompanying the powers of ten. Usually we would take the smaller power of ten as our common power.

● Express 2.0×10^3 as a number times 10^2.

○ $2.0 \times 10^3 = 2.0 \times 10 \times 10 \times 10 = (2.0 \times 10) \times 10^2 = 20 \times 10^2$.

Thus we can rewrite $(2.0 \times 10^3) + (3 \times 10^2)$ as $(20 \times 10^2) + (3 \times 10^2) = (20 + 3) \times 10^2 = 23 \times 10^2$.

● Convert 23×10^2 into scientific notation.

○ $23 \times 10^2 = 2.3 \times 10^3$.

Question 6.4 *Without* using your calculator, try the following additions and subtractions, expressing your answers in scientific notation. Then repeat the calculations *using* your calculator. (Note that the addition and subtraction of negative numbers are described in the maths skills package on the Block 1 CD-ROM, and are also covered in Section 2 of Maths Help in the *SGSG*.)

(a) $(2.3 \times 10^3) + (3.5 \times 10^3)$

(b) $(5.6 \times 10^{-5}) + (2.9 \times 10^{-5})$

(c) $(7.4 \times 10^4) - (4.3 \times 10^4)$

(d) $(7.4 \times 10^4) - (-4.3 \times 10^4)$

(e) $(6.56 \times 10^4) + (3.3 \times 10^3)$

(f) $(7.53 \times 10^6) - (3 \times 10^4)$

(g) $(3.754 \times 10^2) - (3 \times 10^{-1})$ ◀

So much for addition and subtraction; what about multiplication and division?

● $200 \times 300 = 60\,000$; express this equation in scientific notation.

○ $(2 \times 10^2) \times (3 \times 10^2) = 6 \times 10^4$.

Notice that we can write 6×10^4 as $(2 \times 3) \times 10^{(2 + 2)}$ and this gives us a clue as to how to multiply two numbers written in scientific notation.

> When multiplying two numbers written in scientific notation, first *multiply* the two numbers accompanying the powers of ten, then *add* the powers of ten to give the resulting power of ten.

For example, consider the multiplication of 2×10^3 by 4×10^2.

First we multiply the two numbers accompanying the powers of ten:

$(2 \times 10^3) \times (4 \times 10^2) = (2 \times 4) \times (10^3 \times 10^2) = 8 \times (10^3 \times 10^2)$

Adding the two powers of ten, 3 and 2, gives the final power of ten, 5:

$8 \times (10^3 \times 10^2) = 8 \times 10^{(3 + 2)} = 8 \times 10^5$

● What is the result of multiplying 3×10^3 by 3×10^{-1}?

○ First we multiply the two numbers accompanying the powers of ten:

$(3 \times 10^3) \times (3 \times 10^{-1}) = (3 \times 3) \times (10^3 \times 10^{-1}) = 9 \times (10^3 \times 10^{-1})$

Adding the two powers of ten, 3 and −1, gives the final power of ten, 2.

$9 \times (10^3 \times 10^{-1}) = 9 \times 10^{(3 + (-1))} = 9 \times 10^{(3 - 1)} = 9 \times 10^2$

> To divide two numbers written in scientific notation, it is easiest to express the calculation as a fraction. Then first *divide* the two numbers accompanying the powers of ten, and then *subtract* the power of ten of the number on the bottom of the fraction from the power of ten of the number on the top of the fraction.

For example, suppose we want to divide 8×10^5 by 2×10^2:

$$\frac{8 \times 10^5}{2 \times 10^2} = \left(\frac{8}{2}\right) \times \left(\frac{10^5}{10^2}\right)$$

First we divide the two numbers accompanying the powers of ten:

$$\left(\frac{8}{2}\right) \times \left(\frac{10^5}{10^2}\right) = 4 \times \left(\frac{10^5}{10^2}\right)$$

Subtracting the power of ten on the bottom of the fraction (2) from the one on the top (5), i.e. $5 - 2$, gives the final power of ten, 3:

$$4 \times \left(\frac{10^5}{10^2}\right) = 4 \times 10^{(5 - 2)} = 4 \times 10^3$$

● What is the result of dividing 9×10^3 by 3×10^6?

○ First divide the two numbers accompanying the powers of ten:

$$\frac{9 \times 10^3}{3 \times 10^6} = \left(\frac{9}{3}\right) \times \left(\frac{10^3}{10^6}\right) = 3 \times \left(\frac{10^3}{10^6}\right)$$

Subtracting the two powers of ten, $3 - 6 = -3$:

$$3 \times \left(\frac{10^3}{10^6}\right) = 3 \times 10^{(3 - 6)} = 3 \times 10^{-3}$$

Question 6.5 Try the following multiplications and divisions and express your answers in scientific notation. First, avoid using your calculator as much as possible. Then repeat all the calculations using your calculator alone.

(a) $(2.5 \times 10^7) \times (4.0 \times 10^2)$

(b) $(4.2 \times 10^8) \times (3.0 \times 10^{-5})$

(c) $(3.2 \times 10^{-4}) \times (3.0 \times 10^{-3})$

(d) $\dfrac{3.6 \times 10^6}{1.8 \times 10^2}$

(e) $\dfrac{2.4 \times 10^5}{6.0 \times 10^2}$

(f) $\dfrac{2.5 \times 10^3}{5.0 \times 10^7}$

(g) $\dfrac{2.5 \times 10^3}{5.0 \times 10^{-7}}$ ◀

Question 6.6 (a) Express the number of particles in a cubic metre of air at an altitude of 80 km as a percentage of the number in a cubic metre at sea-level.

(b) Express the air pressure at 80 km as a percentage of the air pressure at sea-level.

(c) Describe the trends in Table 6.1 for the variation with increasing altitude of (i) the number of particles in a cubic metre and (ii) the air pressure. ◀

Table 6.1 indicates that as we go to higher altitudes the number of particles in a cubic metre of air and the pressure both decrease. The pressure decreases because it is dependent on the number of particles in a specific volume. However, the number of particles and the pressure do not change in exactly the same way, because the pressure is affected not only by the number of particles but also by the temperature (Box 6.1), which also varies with altitude.

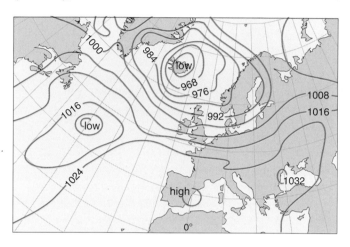

Figure 6.5 A typical map that forms part of a weather forecast. The numbers refer to the pressure at sea-level in millibars.

The pressure at the surface of the Earth, often referred to as the atmospheric pressure, is not constant — it varies slightly from place to place and from day to day. Figure 6.5 is part of a weather forecast which shows how the pressure at sea-level varies across the North Atlantic and Europe. The thin solid lines connect places with the same atmospheric pressure, in much the same way as contours on a map join points of equal height. The pressure contours are known as isobars. The unit of pressure used is the millibar (10^{-3} bar), often abbreviated to mb. Since some properties, such as the boiling temperature of a substance, depend on the atmospheric pressure, we need to define a standard atmospheric pressure at which to measure such properties. By convention this is chosen to be 1 013 mb.

⬤ What is 1 013 mb in bars?

⬤ Since 1 mb = 1×10^{-3} bar, then 1 013 mb = $1\,013 \times 1 \times 10^{-3}$ bar = 1.013 bar. So the standard atmospheric pressure is taken to be 1.013 bar.

The variation in the atmospheric pressure helps forecasters to predict the weather. I can remember my father tapping his barometer, which measured the air pressure. Although he wasn't interested in the numbers, he knew that low pressure is associated with uncertain weather whereas, at least during summer, high pressure is associated with fine weather. A region of very low atmospheric pressure (an 'area of low pressure' on a weather chart) typically has a pressure of about 990 mb, and the eye of a hurricane, an extreme low pressure area, might fall as low as 910 mb. A typical summer anticyclone, a region of high pressure, has a pressure of about 1 040 mb.

6.2.1   Processes in the atmosphere

Now that we know a little more about the atmosphere we can return to the processes, displayed in Figure 5.14, whereby energy is transferred from the Earth's surface to the atmosphere. We shall explain these processes in terms of the particle model.

First, there is conduction and convection. Imagine a 'parcel' (i.e. a fixed mass) of air that is in contact with the ground. The ground has a higher temperature than this air. The energy of the vibrational motion of the particles in the solid ground is greater than the energy of the motion of the particles in the air. When the air particles collide with the ground, energy is transferred to them from the surface particles, so that they move around more quickly. Thus, the temperature of the air is increased, which leads to the parcel of air expanding.

In Section 5.2.1, we used the definition of density (mass/volume) to argue that this thermal expansion will reduce the density of the air. Is this conclusion consistent with the particle model?

Yes. In terms of the particle model, if the volume of a fixed mass of gas increases, there will be fewer particles in a specified volume, so the density decreases.

If the air at the surface becomes sufficiently less dense than that above it, the air at the surface will rise. The columns of rising air break up and so the warmer air mixes with the surrounding cooler air. Thus energy in the hot air is transferred to higher regions by particles in the hot air colliding with other air particles and exchanging energy, as you discovered in Question 6.2. Meanwhile, at the surface of the Earth cold air will have taken the place of the hot air and this new air will start to warm up by conduction. Thus a cycle is set up, with cold air coming to the surface of the Earth and warming up, so that it then rises by convection and warms the atmosphere.

Convection is also involved in a second mechanism by which energy is transferred from the surface to the atmosphere. When water evaporates from the surface of the Earth there needs to be an input of energy from the Earth to free the particles from the liquid state – the latent heat of vaporization. This leads to a cooling of the Earth's surface. The water particles, now in the gaseous state, become part of the rising column of air that cools as it rises. Eventually the air becomes so cold that the water vapour condenses and in so doing releases energy to the atmosphere. As noted earlier, condensation involves the release of an amount of energy equivalent to the energy that was needed to evaporate the water in the first place. Thus energy has been lost from the surface of the Earth and transferred to the atmosphere.

The final mechanism for heating the atmosphere involves the absorption of electromagnetic radiation. In fact, it is the particles in the atmosphere that absorb the radiation, and this increases the energy of the particles.

What happens at the particle level when the atmosphere, the oceans, and the land absorb radiation?

When particles in the atmosphere absorb solar radiation their energy is increased, which leads to the gas particles moving around more quickly. Similarly, when water particles in the ocean absorb radiation they end up moving around more quickly. When solid material on the surface of the Earth absorbs radiation each particle vibrates about a particular point more energetically.

As we shall see in Section 6.5, there are other ways in which these particles are affected when they absorb electromagnetic radiation.

The Earth's atmosphere is not static. Not only is there continuous movement of air vertically between levels, but there is also continuous horizontal movement around the Earth. You may have heard of the jet streams, which are high speed winds encircling the globe at altitudes of approximately 10 km. Closer to the surface there are other winds, again evidence of a dynamic atmosphere. The ultimate cause of these horizontal motions is the greater heating of the Earth's atmosphere and surface in equatorial regions than in polar regions. In equatorial regions the Sun is high in the sky for much of each day, whereas in the polar regions it never reaches far above the horizon. Consequently, over a year, the solar radiation received per unit area of surface is greater in equatorial regions than in polar regions, and so the polar regions are cooler. This difference in temperature leads to differences in pressure and hence to horizontal flows of air. The details are complicated, and will not concern us.

Question 6.7   How does the particle model explain why aeroplanes experience less resistance from the air when they fly at high altitudes compared with when they fly at low altitudes? ◄

Question 6.8   As well as evaporating from the seas, water also 'evaporates' from snow and ice in a process called sublimation (Section 5.2.1); that is, water particles move directly from the solid to the gaseous state. Use the particle model to describe this transformation with the aid of a diagram. Why does it need an input of energy? ◄

Activity 6.5   Applying the particle model

In this activity, you will use the particle model of matter to explain phenomena shown in the video 'Does air have substance?', which you studied in Activity 6.2. ◄

6.3   The composition of the atmosphere

The particle model helps us to explain how the processes of conduction, convection and latent heat transfer affect the temperature of the atmosphere. But we are still a little way from understanding the full effect of the atmosphere on the temperature of the Earth's surface. To make further progress we need to recognize that the atmosphere is actually a **mixture** of *different* gases. In other words, the air around us contains many different types of particle, some of which play an important role in the Earth's greenhouse effect. In this section we refine our model of the atmosphere, and again develop some ideas that are needed for later sections.

Activity 6.6   The composition of the atmosphere

In this activity you will study the video 'The chemical composition of the air', which introduces you to the various components of the Earth's atmosphere. You will also learn about pie charts, which, like graphs, are a way of showing numerical information as pictures. ◄

The information in the pie chart of the composition of the atmosphere in Activity 6.6 is tabulated in Table 6.2. There are other components of the Earth's atmosphere, but these are present only as traces. You can see that the main component is nitrogen, followed by oxygen.

Table 6.2 The gaseous composition of the Earth's atmosphere at sea-level in 1996 (main components only).

Component	Number of particles/ % of total number	Number of particles in a cubic metre	Mass/% of total mass
nitrogen	77.6	2.0×10^{25}	75.5
oxygen	20.9	5.4×10^{24}	23.2
argon	0.93	2.4×10^{23}	1.28
water[a]	0.5	1.3×10^{23}	0.3
carbon dioxide	3.6×10^{-2}	9.2×10^{21}	5.3×10^{-2}

[a] Highly variable, so average values are given.

If air is made up of a number of components, how does this affect our particle model of the air? Since the atmosphere consists of very many particles, and since it is a mixture of different components, it must be a mixture of different types of particle. The relative numbers of each type of particle in Table 6.2 show that the air consists almost entirely of nitrogen particles and oxygen particles, with smaller numbers of argon, water and carbon dioxide particles. In Table 6.2 the percentage composition based on the number of particles is different from the percentage composition by mass because the different types of particle have different masses. Question 6.9 will help you to understand why these percentages are different.

Question 6.9 Figure 6.6 shows a mixture of red and blue particles. Each red particle has a mass of 1 g, whereas the blue particles each have a mass of 10 g. Calculate the percentages of red and blue particles in the mixture (a) based on the numbers of particles, and (b) based on their masses. ◄

The first column of Table 6.2 shows that if we took a sample of 100 particles of air then, *on average*, there would be about 78 particles of nitrogen and 21 particles of oxygen. It also suggests that, *on average*, there are 0.9 particles of argon, 0.5 particles of water and 3.6×10^{-2} particles of carbon dioxide. Clearly this is unhelpful, because there is no such thing in reality as a fraction of a particle; it reflects our choice of 100 particles as the starting point. For such small proportions it is better to start with a million, as described in Box 6.3, *Parts per million*.

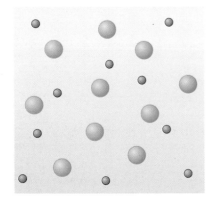

Figure 6.6 A collection of 10 red particles of mass 1 g each, and 10 blue particles of mass 10 g each.

Box 6.3 Parts per million

As you saw in Box 2.4 of Block 1, we can describe a proportion in various ways. Suppose we have a crowd of 100 people, 50 men and 50 women. Here we can express the proportions quite easily using fractions: $\frac{50}{100}$, i.e. half, of the crowd are men and half are women. Now suppose there are 49 men and 51 women. The fraction of men is now $\frac{49}{100}$ and the fraction of women $\frac{51}{100}$. The fractions start to become awkward. One way round this is to express the proportion as a percentage, that is the number of hundredths — there are 49% men and 51% women.

Now suppose the crowd is bigger, a million people, of which 493 858 are men and 506 142 are women. The percentage of men is now 49.3858% and the percentage of women is 50.6142%, and these would be quoted as 49% and 51% to two significant figures. So percentages can still cope with these bigger numbers. However, suppose that in the crowd of a million there are only 13 people called Andrew who are wearing blue trousers; this proportion would be $\frac{13}{10^6} \times 100\% = 0.0013\%$. A better way of expressing such small proportions is to use **parts per million**, abbreviated to **p.p.m.** Just as a percentage expresses the number of hundredths, so parts per million express the number of millionths. Thus, the proportion of people whose name is Andrew and who are wearing blue trousers is thirteen millionths or thirteen parts per million.

● Suppose the crowd consisted of 5 million people, of whom 35 were called Abigail and wore black trousers. What proportion is this in parts per million?

● Since 35 people out of five million are called Abigail and wear black trousers, then on average out of one million, there would be 7 people called Abigail who wear black trousers. Thus the proportion is $\frac{35}{5 \times 10^6}$ or $\frac{7}{10^6}$, i.e. 7 p.p.m.

● Table 6.2 shows that the percentage of argon particles in air is 0.93%. Express this as a fraction, and as a proportion in p.p.m. How many particles of argon will there be, on average, in a million particles of air?

● To convert 0.93% into a fraction we divide by 100 (Box 2.4 in Block 1): $\frac{0.93}{100}$

To convert this fraction into p.p.m., we multiply it by a million:

$$\frac{0.93}{100} \times 1\,000\,000 = 0.93 \times 10\,000 = 9\,300 \text{ p.p.m.}$$

So out of every million particles of air there are 9 300 particles of argon.

There are also 5 000 particles of water, on average, and 360 particles of carbon dioxide in every million particles of air, so in parts per million the proportions of water and carbon dioxide particles in the atmosphere are 5 000 p.p.m. and 360 p.p.m., respectively. In all subsequent discussion the proportions of the various components in the atmosphere will be expressed in terms of the number of particles. When discussing the proportions of nitrogen and oxygen we will favour the use of percentages, but when discussing the proportions of the minor constituents in the atmosphere we will use parts per million.

Figure 6.7 gives visual expression to the data in the final column of Table 6.2, namely that the atmosphere consists mainly of nitrogen particles (dark blue in Figure 6.7) plus a smaller number of oxygen particles (red), but very few argon (pale blue), water (green) and carbon dioxide (black) particles.

However, this begs the question of how these particles differ. The answer to this brings us to one of the most important ideas in science:

All such particles are made from atoms.

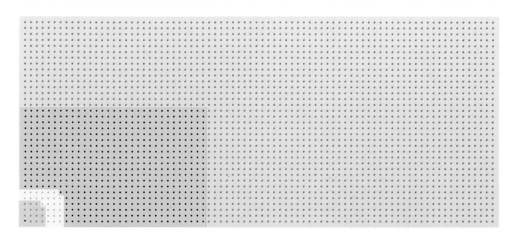

Figure 6.7 The particle composition of the atmosphere, showing the proportions of the different types of particle.

6.3.1   Atoms and molecules

All matter is composed of **atoms**, which for the moment we will consider as hard spheres. They are very small, roughly 10^{-10} m across. A page of this book is about 200 000 atoms thick, and 40 million iron atoms placed side-by-side would form a line only about 1 cm long. Recently, images of individual atoms have been obtained (Figure 6.8). Although all matter is made of atoms, not all atoms are the same. There are about a hundred or so different types of atom, including oxygen atoms, nitrogen atoms, carbon atoms, hydrogen atoms, argon atoms and iron atoms, which provide us with the basic building blocks from which everything in the world is made. It is like having a 'lego' set with about a hundred different types of brick. By using different atoms, or joining them in different ways, you can produce, for example, water, salt, glass or a tree — or anything else you like to name in the whole Universe!

Figure 6.8   An image of a ring of 48 iron atoms on a copper surface, obtained using an instrument known as a scanning tunnelling microscope. This technique shows the positions of the atoms but not their shape.

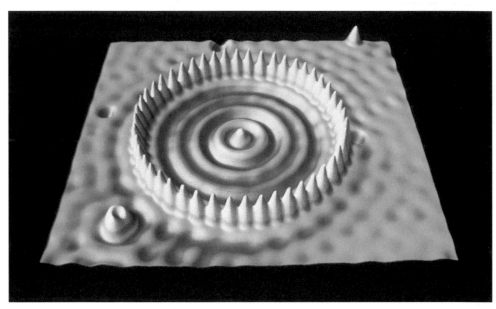

Atoms are the smallest entities of substances known as **chemical elements**, or **elements** for short. Table 6.3 lists some of the well-known elements. Each chemical element consists of just one type of atom. For example, pure copper contains only copper atoms and pure silver contains silver atoms alone. So there are a hundred or so different elements. *It is not possible to convert one chemical element into another by chemical means.*

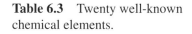 Lead and gold are both chemical elements. Was the alchemist's dream of converting lead into gold ever going to be achievable?

No; as we have just stated, it is not possible to convert one chemical element, like lead, into another, such as gold, using chemical means.

Five of the elements listed in Table 6.3 — argon, chlorine, hydrogen, nitrogen and oxygen — are gases under normal conditions of temperature and pressure. But only one of these, argon, exists as single atoms, represented as a pale blue sphere in Figure 6.9a. The smallest particle of each of the other gaseous elements in Table 6.3 is a **molecule**. The molecules of chlorine, hydrogen, nitrogen and oxygen each consist of two atoms of the element joined or 'bonded' together. Thus, the main atmospheric constituent, nitrogen, does not exist as single atoms, but as nitrogen atoms bonded together in pairs, which can be represented as shown in Figure 6.9b. The point to

Table 6.3   Twenty well-known chemical elements.

aluminium	lead
argon	mercury
calcium	nickel
carbon	nitrogen
chlorine	oxygen
copper	platinum
gold	silicon
hydrogen	silver
iodine	tin
iron	zinc

grasp is that splitting this 'nitrogen particle' further — to give individual nitrogen atoms — would produce *a different substance with different properties* from the nitrogen in the air. Similarly, oxygen in the air exists as pairs of oxygen atoms, as shown in Figure 6.9c. However, whether an element consists of single atoms, or combinations of two (or more) atoms of the same type joined together, it is still an element.

The world of atoms and molecules is primarily the domain of the chemist. You will learn more about this exciting world in Blocks 6 and 8. For now, it is sufficient to note that the images in Figure 6.9 are based on a **'ball-and-stick' representation** of the structure of matter at the atomic level. The essential features of this type of representation are as follows.

- The atomic 'lego-set' from which all real molecules are constructed is represented as a series of hard spheres or 'balls', different colours being used to distinguish the various types of atom.

- As you will discover later, the atoms in a real molecule are joined to one another by **chemical bonds**, or **bonds** for short. Each bond in a molecule is represented by inserting a 'stick' between the two atoms involved, as indicated in parts (b) and (c) of Figure 6.9.

Depicting molecules as collections of balls and sticks represents an important refinement of the simple particle model. It allows chemists to convey a good deal more information about the nature of the particles that make up a given substance. This is evident in the simple examples collected in Figure 6.9. But the value of the ball-and-stick representation becomes more apparent once we turn our attention to substances in which the molecule is built up from *more than one type* of atom. Such substances are *not* elements; they are known as **chemical compounds**, or **compounds** for short. Most of the substances in the world around you fall into this category, as do two of the atmospheric constituents included in Table 6.2 — water and carbon dioxide.

As we reminded you earlier, the smallest entity of water is a water molecule. All water molecules are identical: each one is constructed from one oxygen atom and two hydrogen atoms. Furthermore, there is experimental evidence that these three atoms are linked together as shown by the ball-and-stick representation in Figure 6.10a. Notice that this representation conveys the following information about the water molecule:

- water is a chemical compound, because there is more than one type of atom present;

- the oxygen atom is bonded to *both* of the hydrogen atoms, as indicated by the two sticks;

- the two hydrogen atoms are *not* bonded to one another — they are not joined by a stick;

- the molecule has a *shape* — specifically, it is bent (i.e. the three atoms are not arranged in a straight line).

- A ball-and-stick representation of a carbon dioxide molecule is shown in Figure 6.10b. List the information about carbon dioxide that is conveyed by this representation.

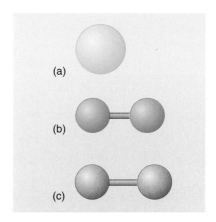

Figure 6.9 Three of the gaseous elements in the air, shown in the ball-and-stick representation. Argon (a) exists as single atoms, but nitrogen (b) and oxygen (c) both exist as pairs of atoms. Pale blue, dark blue and red have been used to distinguish the atoms of argon, nitrogen and oxygen, respectively.

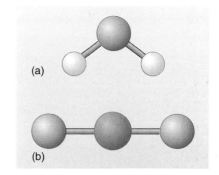

Figure 6.10 Ball-and-stick representations of (a) a water molecule — oxygen and hydrogen atoms are represented by red and pale grey balls, respectively, and (b) a carbon dioxide molecule — carbon and oxygen atoms are represented by dark grey and red balls, respectively.

○ There are four main points:

- carbon dioxide is a chemical compound, because the molecule is made up of more than one type of atom;
- the molecule contains three atoms — one carbon atom and two oxygen atoms;
- the carbon atom is bonded to both of the oxygen atoms, but the latter are not bonded to one another;
- the molecule is linear, not bent like the water molecule.

The important general point to come out of the examples in Figure 6.10 is that real molecules have a well-defined composition, structure, *and* shape. Each type of molecule is constructed from certain atoms, which are not only held together by a specific number of bonds, but also arranged relative to one another in space in a particular way. The ball-and-stick representation captures all of these aspects of molecular structure.

Figure 6.11 shows a modified version of our model of the composition of the atmosphere in Figure 6.7. By using the ball-and-stick representation we can give some shape to the particles, and can show which atoms are involved in which particles and how they are joined together. Figure 6.11 shows that air is a mixture of gases — that is it contains more than one type of molecule.

Note that a chemical compound is not a mixture because, although it is made up of more than one type of atom, only one type of molecule is present. For example, pure carbon dioxide contains only carbon dioxide molecules.

Question 6.10 Figure 6.12 shows two samples of ten oxygen atoms and twenty hydrogen atoms, arranged in different ways. How would you describe each sample? ◀

Figure 6.11 The particle composition of the atmosphere, with an indication of the shapes of the particles and of which atoms are bonded together in each type of particle.

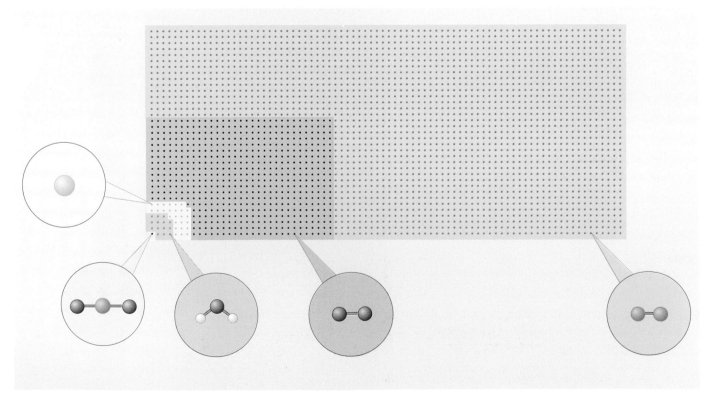

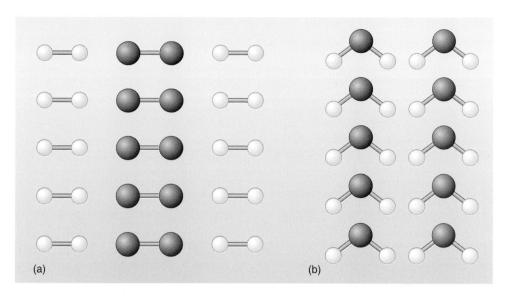

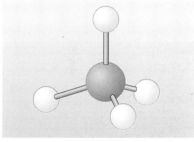

Figure 6.12 Two samples of ten oxygen atoms and twenty hydrogen atoms. Note that the colour code is as in Figures 6.9 and 6.10.

(a)

(b)

Question 6.11 Figure 6.13 shows a ball-and-stick representation of methane — a trace constituent of the atmosphere. In this representation, as in the molecule, the bonds do *not* lie in one plane, and so Figure 6.13 is actually a two-dimensional drawing of a three-dimensional structure.

(a) Is methane a chemical element or a chemical compound?

(b) Which elements are present in methane?

(c) How many atoms of each element are there in a molecule of methane?

(d) How many bonds are there, and which atoms do the bonds join together?

Figure 6.13 The structure of methane. Note that the colour code is as in Figures 6.9 and 6.10.

6.4 Properties of gases in the Earth's atmosphere

Having learnt a little about the molecular make-up of the gases in the atmosphere, we now take a brief look at some of the properties of these gases.

6.4.1 Oxygen

One key property of oxygen is its chemical reactivity. Given the right circumstances, it can combine with many other elements to give chemical compounds. For example, coal is mainly made up of carbon atoms. When we burn coal, carbon atoms in the coal combine with oxygen atoms from the oxygen molecules in the air to form carbon dioxide molecules. We call this transformation of one substance into another a **chemical reaction**, which we can write simply as:

oxygen and carbon *react to form* carbon dioxide (6.2)

In this chemical reaction, the carbon and oxygen are referred to as the **reactants** and carbon dioxide as the **product**. As you will see in Section 10, the burning of so-called fossil fuels, such as coal, has an important effect on the GMST.

Petrol is derived from crude oil, another fossil fuel. Petrol is a mixture of different molecules, each type of molecule consisting of carbon and hydrogen atoms. It also burns in the air, as follows:

oxygen and petrol *react to form* water and carbon dioxide (6.3)

91

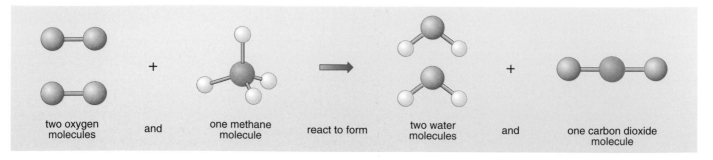

two oxygen molecules   and   one methane molecule   react to form   two water molecules   and   one carbon dioxide molecule

Figure 6.14 The molecules involved in the reaction between oxygen and methane. The colour code is as in Figures 6.9 and 6.10.

What are the reactants and products in reaction 6.3?

Petrol and oxygen are the reactants and carbon dioxide and water are the products.

Natural gas is a fossil fuel consisting mainly of methane, the structure of which you met in Figure 6.13. We can express the burning of methane in air as:

oxygen and methane *react to form* water and carbon dioxide   (6.4)

The molecules involved in this chemical reaction are shown in Figure 6.14. Notice that in going from reactants to products the atoms have exchanged partners. For example, in the reactants each oxygen atom is bonded to another oxygen atom. However, in the products each oxygen atom becomes bonded to either a hydrogen atom or a carbon atom. In this reaction, existing bonds are broken and new bonds are made.

According to the representation in Figure 6.14, how many atoms of carbon, oxygen and hydrogen are there in the reactants, methane and oxygen, and in the products, carbon dioxide and water?

Figure 6.14 shows that one molecule of methane reacts with two molecules of oxygen. Thus the reactants contain one carbon atom, four hydrogen atoms and four oxygen atoms. The products are one molecule of carbon dioxide and two molecules of water, which also contain one carbon atom, four hydrogen atoms and four oxygen atoms.

Notice that we have the same number of atoms of each element in the reactants as in the products. This is a feature of all chemical reactions, which can be summed up in the simple rule:

During a chemical reaction, atoms are neither created nor destroyed.

Will carbon react with oxygen to form water?

No. Water molecules contain hydrogen atoms (Figure 6.14), and thus water will never be one product of a reaction between the elements carbon and oxygen.

We use fossil fuels, such as methane, to provide energy, for example to heat a building or to power a car. The energy is released as a result of the reaction between the fuel and oxygen in the air, so we can extend our description:

oxygen and fuel *react to form* water and carbon dioxide, and energy is released

(6.5)

Notice that the fuel is not converted in some way into energy. The fuel reacts with oxygen in the air to give other materials — the atoms have swapped partners to give carbon dioxide and water. The energy released comes from the breaking and making of chemical bonds.

Oxygen also has an important role in life. When we breathe, we expand our lungs, which draw in air. In the lungs are very narrow blood vessels, which are porous to the air and enable oxygen to be absorbed into the blood. Thus, the air we breathe out has had some of the oxygen removed from it. Oxygen is needed in the human body for a number of reasons. Just as with fossil fuels, oxygen reacts with substances in the body to give water and carbon dioxide, and energy is released. Of course, the substances don't actually 'burn' in the body: the chemical reaction is carried out in a much more controlled fashion, but the result is the same. The water produced becomes part of our general store of water, but the carbon dioxide is transported in the bloodstream to the lungs where it is transferred to the air and exhaled.

Although here we have concentrated on humans, you saw in Block 1 that this use of oxygen is crucial for all animals, including fish, which use oxygen that is dissolved in the water around them.

○ Why do you think it is difficult for animals adapted to living at low altitudes to breathe at high altitudes? (Assume that the relative proportions of the major gases do not change much with altitude.)

○ As you saw in Table 6.1, at higher altitudes there are fewer particles per cubic metre in the atmosphere, and so there will be fewer oxygen molecules. At higher altitudes there will be less oxygen entering the bloodstream with each breath, so animals have to breathe more deeply and more often at higher altitudes, to get the same amount of oxygen.

6.4.2 Nitrogen and argon

As noted earlier, nitrogen exists in the atmosphere as nitrogen molecules, each containing two nitrogen atoms (Figure 6.9b). Unlike oxygen, one of the key properties of nitrogen is that it is relatively unreactive, that is, it does not readily combine with other substances. For this reason nitrogen is often used to 'blanket' flammable materials as a safety measure. It is also used in the storage of foods — you sometimes see on the labels of packets that the foodstuff is stored or packed under nitrogen. This is because nitrogen does not support life. Many bacteria can't live for long in pure nitrogen.

Argon exists in the atmosphere as single atoms (Figure 6.9a). This is because it does not combine, or react, with itself or other elements. It is a member of a class of substances known as the noble gases, because they are so unreactive — they want nothing to do with other elements. All noble gases exist as single atoms in the gaseous state. Helium, neon and krypton are other examples of noble gases.

6.4.3 Water and carbon dioxide

You have seen that water and carbon dioxide are produced when fossil fuels are burnt in air. Neither of them reacts particularly well with any of the other gases in the atmosphere although, as you will see in Section 8, they are both involved in one process that is crucial for life on Earth.

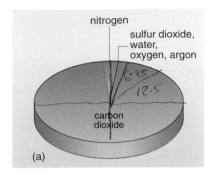

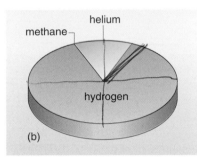

Figure 6.15 Pie charts of the main components of the atmospheres of (a) Venus and (b) Jupiter.

You may be aware that water is often represented by the shorthand form H_2O, pronounced 'aitch two oh'. This is because, as Figure 6.10a shows, a molecule of water contains *two H*ydrogen atoms and *one O*xygen atom. For a similar reason carbon dioxide is often referred to as CO_2, pronounced 'see oh two'. We shall examine the role of water and carbon dioxide in the atmosphere in more depth in Sections 7 and 8, and there you will often see them referred to by the symbols H_2O and CO_2. Symbols like these are part of the language of chemistry, which you will meet again in later blocks.

6.4.4 Air as a mixture

Our atmosphere is a mixture of gases, and the properties of the atmosphere reflect the combined properties of the individual gases that make up air. Although the air is mainly nitrogen, it contains enough oxygen for us to live. However, in a mixture the properties of the pure gas are often diminished, that is the properties can be observed but to a lesser extent. For example, although a biscuit will burn vigorously in pure oxygen, it will not ignite so readily in the air!

Question 6.12   Figure 6.15 shows pie charts of the main components of the atmospheres of two of the Sun's planets, Venus and Jupiter. Estimate the percentages of the gases in the atmosphere of each of the two planets, to the nearest 5%. ◀

The answer to Question 6.12 mentioned the element hydrogen. Hydrogen gas exists as hydrogen molecules, each containing two hydrogen atoms (Figure 6.12a). Hydrogen reacts with oxygen to give water, as shown in Figure 6.16. Again energy is released in this reaction. Hydrogen is less dense than air and was used in airships at one time. It was hydrogen that was used in the Hindenburg airship, which caught fire after crossing the Atlantic on 6 May 1937, with the loss of 36 lives. Even now, hydrogen still has a role in travel, since it is used as a fuel in the space shuttle! Liquid hydrogen and liquid oxygen provide one of the best propellant mixtures, giving the greatest 'bounce per ounce'. Unfortunately, the high pressures and low temperatures needed to ensure that the hydrogen and oxygen remain liquid make their use quite limited.

Figure 6.16   The reaction between hydrogen and oxygen at the molecular level.

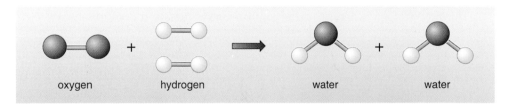

oxygen   hydrogen   water   water

Question 6.13   Helium is less dense than air and nowadays is preferred to hydrogen in airships. Why do you think this is? ◀

Question 6.14   Why do you think carbon dioxide and water are produced when methane reacts with oxygen, but only water is produced when hydrogen reacts with oxygen? ◀

Question 6.15   Based on the previous discussion of the various gases, how easy would it be for us to breathe the atmosphere or light a fire on Venus or Jupiter? ◀

Question 6.16   The reaction between petrol and oxygen provides the energy to move a car. Oxygen is supplied through the air intake and petrol is provided from the fuel tank. What is expelled from the exhaust? ◀

6.5   The greenhouse gases

We have now finished our lengthy diversion into the composition and properties of the atmosphere and can return to our original theme of the Earth's surface temperature. Look back at Figure 5.14. One of the important mechanisms by which energy is transferred to and from the atmosphere is by the absorption and emission of radiation.

⬤ What happens when the surface of the Earth absorbs either solar radiation or infrared radiation emitted by the atmosphere?

⬤ In both cases, the absorption of radiation leads to an input of energy to the Earth's surface. By itself, this would lead to an increase in the surface temperature.

⬤ Which type of radiation is strongly absorbed by the Earth's atmosphere, and why is this important for the GMST?

⬤ The atmosphere is a strong absorber of longwave infrared radiation, and thus captures and recycles most of the radiation emitted by the Earth's surface. If this were not the case, there would be no greenhouse effect and the Earth's surface would be considerably cooler than it actually is.

As we hinted in Section 5.4.3, only certain gases in the atmosphere actually absorb infrared radiation. A molecule can absorb infrared radiation in two ways. The chemical bonds that hold molecules together are like springs and, like springs, they can vibrate, as shown in Figure 6.17 for water. When the bond (or spring) absorbs energy from the infrared radiation it vibrates more energetically. However, for reasons that are beyond our scope, infrared radiation is absorbed only if a molecule contains more than two atoms, or — if it contains only two atoms — the atoms at each end of the bond are of different elements. Note that to use the 'ball-and-stick' representation in relation to vibrations, it has had to be developed so that the bonds between the atoms in a molecule are not rigid sticks, but springs.

⬤ Which of the atmospheric constituents in Table 6.2 can absorb infrared radiation through changes in their vibration? (Figures 6.9 and 6.10 can help you to decide.)

⬤ Argon exists as single atoms. Therefore there are no bonds, and so it will not absorb infrared radiation. Oxygen and nitrogen molecules consist of two atoms of the *same* element attached by a bond (Figure 6.9), so these molecules will not absorb infrared radiation. Molecules of carbon dioxide and water both contain more than two atoms — so these compounds will absorb infrared radiation through changes in the way they vibrate.

The second way in which molecules can absorb infrared radiation is via *rotation* of the molecule. If infrared radiation is absorbed, the molecule will rotate faster. Of the atmospheric gases listed in Table 6.2, only water can absorb infrared radiation in this way.

We conclude that nitrogen, oxygen and argon absorb very little infrared radiation, so they will not behave as greenhouse gases. Water vapour and carbon dioxide do absorb infrared radiation and so they *are* greenhouse gases. This is an amazing result. The predominant gases in the Earth's atmosphere, nitrogen and oxygen, which together account for almost 99% of the atmosphere, make no contribution to the greenhouse effect. However two minor components, carbon dioxide (0.036%) and water (0.5%)

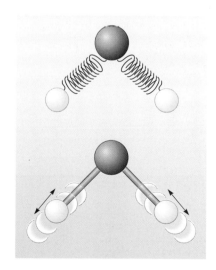

Figure 6.17   A water molecule where the bonds are represented as springs. The double-headed arrows show how the bond (or spring) can vibrate.

cause most of the considerable increase in the GMST attributed to the greenhouse effect. The larger contribution (about 60%) comes from water vapour.

The amounts of these two gases in the atmosphere are very important. The amount of infrared radiation absorbed depends on how many water molecules and carbon dioxide molecules are present in the atmosphere: the more molecules present, the greater the proportion of radiation absorbed. Look back at Figure 5.14. If there were less water vapour and carbon dioxide in the atmosphere, then we might predict that less of the outgoing infrared radiation would be absorbed and more would escape directly to space. The atmosphere would then *emit* less radiation, because less had been absorbed. This would lead to a reduction in the amount of radiation absorbed by the Earth's surface. This alone would result in a lower GMST. Thus, the greenhouse effect would be reduced. We can also suggest that if there were more carbon dioxide and water vapour in the atmosphere, more infrared radiation would be absorbed and thus more would be emitted, and so the greenhouse effect would be greater — there would be a higher GMST. You will get a chance to test these predictions for yourself in Section 9.

We started this block by examining the temperature of the surface of the Earth and the factors that control it. Our quest has led us to identify two of the key factors: the amounts of water vapour and carbon dioxide in the atmosphere. As scientists we do not stop here; we must continue our search and ask the further question — what controls the small, but important, amounts of water vapour and carbon dioxide in the atmosphere? In the next two sections we will address this question: in Section 7 for water vapour, and in Section 8 for carbon dioxide.

Question 6.17   Neon, a noble gas, is present in the Earth's atmosphere at a level of 18 p.p.m., and methane is present at a level of 1.72 p.p.m. Are these two gases likely to be greenhouse gases? ◄

Question 6.18   In Question 6.12, you saw that the atmosphere of Venus is about 97% carbon dioxide. The Venusian atmosphere contains far more particles per cubic metre than the Earth's. Would you expect there to be a greenhouse effect on Venus? If so, how would it compare with that on Earth? ◄

 Activity 6.7   Summary of the composition and properties of air
At the start of Section 6 you wrote down what you knew about the air (Activity 6.1). In this activity, you will summarize what you now know about the air, and compare this with your previous knowledge. ◄

6.6 Summary of Section 6

Some important properties of solids, liquids and gases can be explained in terms of a simple particle model of matter. This model also helps to explain the changes of state that take place when the temperature is changed and the origin of the pressure exerted by a gas.

The pressure and the number of particles per cubic metre of the atmosphere decrease with increasing altitude.

Vertical differences in the temperature of the atmosphere lead to convection of air and thus to exchange of energy between the surface and the atmosphere. The particle model can be used to explain how evaporation of water at the Earth's surface and condensation in the atmosphere help to transfer energy through the atmosphere via latent heat.

Molecules, the smallest particles of solids, liquids and gases, are made of atoms. They can be represented by ball-and-stick models.

The Earth's atmosphere is a mixture of different gases — elements and compounds. Molecules of elements consist of only one type of atom, whereas molecules of chemical compounds consist of more than one type of atom, bonded together.

A chemical reaction involves the conversion of reactants into products. Atoms are neither created nor destroyed in this process, but 'change partners'. Reactions can release energy.

Some of the properties of air can be predicted from the properties of its constituent gases.

Although oxygen and nitrogen, the predominant gases in the Earth's atmosphere, do not absorb infrared radiation, two minor constituents, carbon dioxide (0.036%) and water vapour (0.5%), do absorb infrared radiation, and are the main greenhouse gases.

There are simple rules for doing calculations involving powers of ten.

Parts per million is a good way of expressing the amount of a component that is present in a small proportion.

Pie charts can be used to provide a visual representation of relative proportions.

7 The water cycle

In the last section you saw that, although there is only a relatively small amount of water vapour in the Earth's atmosphere, the fact that it absorbs outgoing infrared radiation means that its presence has a major effect on the GMST. It is the main greenhouse gas.

○ In what other way does water vapour in the atmosphere influence the GMST?

○ Water vapour in the atmosphere can form clouds, which reflect solar radiation and so reduce the amount that reaches the ground.

Clearly, we need to know what influences the amount of water vapour in the atmosphere and whether this amount varies in the short and long term. This in turn requires us to examine how water gets into and out of the atmosphere. As you might expect from your reading of Block 1, we must first look at how water, in all its various forms, is distributed on the Earth.

○ Give some examples of different forms in which water occurs around the Earth.

○ Water exists in the gaseous state (water vapour) in the atmosphere, as liquid water droplets or solid ice crystals in clouds, as liquid water in the oceans, lakes, rivers and underground, and as solid ice in snow, glaciers and ice-sheets.

One of the most important aspects of the occurrence of water on the Earth is the fact that it is not static. There is a continuous exchange of water between the oceans, atmosphere, lakes, streams, surface ice and clouds. Figures 4.17 and 6.2 in Block 1 provided an overview of many of the features of this system, which is called the water cycle. Our approach in this section is to develop a more complete cycle, with an emphasis on processes involving water vapour in the atmosphere. Our aim is to develop your understanding of how the amount of water vapour in the atmosphere is controlled, and to describe how, and to what extent, it could be changed.

7.1 Precipitation

One of the more obvious ways in which we see water being exchanged within the water cycle is when it rains. Block 1 described how rain is formed in the atmosphere. Here we shall examine this process in a little more detail. To that end we shall use the weather forecast for the UK shown in Figure 7.1. This shows that the UK is under the influence of westerly winds — that is, winds that blow from the west — and so air moves from over the Atlantic Ocean, across the west coast and towards the east. In western Scotland, the Lake District and Wales there are mountains close to the coast, and so the air needs to rise to get over these obstructions. As the air rises its temperature decreases — at an average rate of about 1 °C per 100 m of altitude.

○ To pass over the highlands of Scotland the air needs to rise by about 1 000 m. By how many degrees will it then cool?

○ Since the air cools by an average of 1 °C per 100 m, a rise of 1 000 m corresponds to a cooling of about $\frac{1\,000\,\text{m}}{100\,\text{m}} \times 1\,°\text{C} = 10\,°\text{C}$.

The maximum amount of water that the air can contain decreases as the temperature decreases, and so the amount of water in the air coming off the ocean at, say, 20 °C

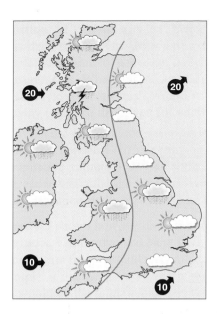

Figure 7.1 A typical weather forecast for the UK, of the type that appears daily in the newspapers. The numbers indicate wind speed (in miles per hour) and the arrows show wind direction.

will probably be too much for the air to hold at, say, 10 °C. The water thus condenses. This condensation is promoted by dust, and other small particles, suspended in the air, around which the condensation occurs. When this formation of small water droplets occurs on a very large scale, a cloud is formed. These very small droplets slowly coalesce to form larger droplets and eventually they may become so big that they can no longer stay in the cloud, and so they fall as rain. This formation of clouds near the west coast explains why the forecast in Figure 7.1 predicted rain in Scotland, northwest England, and Wales.

○ What questions does this explanation of the formation of rain leave unanswered?

○ You may have wondered why the small droplets didn't fall as rain or why we get different types of rain — light or heavy rain. This explanation does not account for why some clouds pass overhead without dropping water, whereas other clouds produce a huge downpour.

In fact the formation of rain is a complex process, which is why it is so difficult to predict. We cannot go into the details here.

The more general term is precipitation, which includes any form of water, liquid or solid, that originates from the atmosphere and ends up on the ground. Examples include rain, hail, snow, dew or hoar frost. As you saw in Block 1, hail is frozen raindrops, and snow arises from clouds in which water vapour condensed directly to the solid state. When the air at ground level cools rapidly, water vapour may condense from the air to give the liquid droplets that we know as dew, and if it condenses below its freezing temperature we get hoar frost.

How much precipitation falls on average on the Earth's surface in a year? In answering this question we start by considering a single location. To measure precipitation, all forms of water must be included — rain, snow, hail, dew, and frost. The rain gauge experiment (Activity 2.1) introduced you to how this can be done at a single location. The total for a year is called the annual precipitation. Activity 2.1 also shows that the precipitation in one week is usually somewhat different from the precipitation in another week. Even though a year is a longer span of time, it is still the case that, at a given location, the precipitation in one year is usually different

Box 7.2 *More about powers*

You should be familiar with the fact that $\frac{1}{10^3} = 10^{-3}$ (Block 1, Box 6.2). When the 10 is brought from the bottom of the fraction to the top, the sign of the power is changed from plus to minus, i.e. the 3 changes to –3. In the same way, $\frac{1}{3^2} = 3^{-2}$ and $\frac{1}{m^3} = m^{-3}$.

This procedure of *reversing* the sign of a power when a quantity is moved from the bottom of a fraction to the top applies equally well to cases where we start with a negative power on the bottom of a fraction. Thus $\frac{1}{10^{-3}} = 10^3$, and this can easily be confirmed:

$$\frac{1}{10^{-3}} = \frac{1}{0.001} = \frac{1000}{1} = 10^3$$

In the same way,

$$\frac{1}{3^{-2}} = 3^2 \text{ and } \frac{1}{m^{-3}} = m^3$$

This is consistent with what you learnt in Box 6.2 about division of numbers involving powers of ten.

○ How do we perform the calculation $\frac{10^5}{10^2}$?

○ We subtract the power of ten on the bottom of the fraction (2) from the power on the top (5):

$$\frac{10^5}{10^2} = 10^{5-2} = 10^3$$

Suppose we apply this rule to work out $\frac{1}{10^{-4}}$, which is the same as $1 \div 10^{-4}$. Using the fact that $10^0 = 1$ (Block 1, Box 6.2), we can write

$$\frac{1}{10^{-4}} = \frac{10^0}{10^{-4}} = 10^{0-(-4)} = 10^{0+4} = 10^4$$

The key point to remember is:

> when you move a power from the bottom of a fraction to the top, then you must reverse the sign of the power from + to −, or from − to +.

$$\frac{1}{10^{-2}} = 10^{2} \quad \text{reverse the sign} \qquad \frac{1}{10^{2}} = 10^{-2} \quad \text{reverse the sign}$$

$$\frac{1}{m^{2}} = m^{-2} \quad \text{reverse the sign} \qquad \frac{1}{m^{-2}} = m^{2} \quad \text{reverse the sign}$$

○ Simplify the following quantities by bringing the quantity on the bottom of the fraction to the top: (a) $\frac{1}{2^4}$; (b) $\frac{1}{5^{-2}}$; (c) $\frac{3}{m^{-3}}$.

○ (a) 2^{-4}; (b) 5^2; (c) $3\,m^3$.

7.2.2 Land and ocean

Evaporation is the process by which water is transferred from the land and oceans to the atmosphere. Stop for a moment and think about which factors affect how easily water evaporates from the surface of the Earth.

○ Figure 7.6 shows the monthly evaporation of water from a lake in the UK over a year. How does the evaporation change during the year, and why do you think it varies in this way?

○ The monthly evaporation is greater in the summer than in the winter. The key factor that causes this will be the temperature; you know from experience that puddles evaporate more quickly during the summer than in the winter, so the monthly total will be greater in the summer.

As we saw earlier, there is a maximum amount of water that the air can contain at any one temperature. Air that holds as much water vapour as it can take is said to be saturated. (In Block 1 you met the concept of water being saturated with dissolved oxygen in the context of Figure 6.9.) However, the air is not always saturated, and a term that is often used to express the extent to which the air is saturated is *relative*

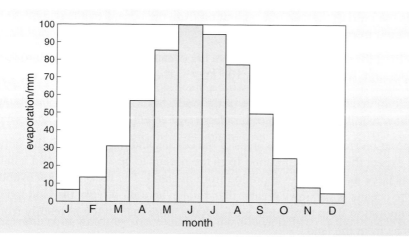

Figure 7.6   Typical monthly evaporation from a lake in East Anglia.

humidity. This expresses the mass of water in the air as a percentage of the mass of water in saturated air at the same temperature. Thus if the relative humidity is 50%, the mass of water in the air is half of what it would contain if it were saturated.

Just how easily water evaporates into the air depends on how far the air is from being completely saturated. This is why wind and convection are other important factors controlling evaporation. The air in contact with liquid (or solid) water will become saturated and, unless there is some mechanism for replacing it with less saturated air, evaporation will slow down. Wind and convection carry saturated air away, replacing it with less saturated air that can take up more water by evaporation. This is one of the reasons why washing hanging outside dries more quickly on windy days.

- Is the percentage of water vapour in the air likely to be greater over oceans or over land, assuming the temperature is the same in both cases and that the air is not saturated?

- The extent of evaporation will depend on the surface area of water that is in contact with the air. Clearly, this is usually greater over the oceans, so the percentage of water vapour in the atmosphere over oceans is generally greater than that over land.

We can demonstrate this difference by subdividing the flow diagram in Figure 7.5 to give Figure 7.7, in which we have separated the precipitation and evaporation over land from that over the oceans. (Transpiration will be explained shortly.)

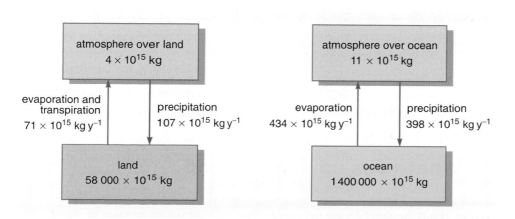

Figure 7.7   A flow diagram to show the exchange of water between the atmosphere, land and ocean. The numbers in the boxes refer to the mass in kilograms of water in that particular reservoir. The numbers on the arrows refer to the movement of water from one reservoir to another in kilograms per year.

Coal formation on land

There is another major process by which carbon can become part of the rock reservoir — coal formation. Plant material that falls on water-saturated soil in peatlands, swamps, marshes and other wetland environments decomposes only very slowly. This stored carbon can be rapidly released as CO_2 if oxygen reaches the peat; this can occur, for instance, if the water supply to a wetland is reduced (even temporarily) and the saturated soil dries out. Under the right circumstances, however, carbon deposited in wetlands can be stored for a very long time.

The 'right circumstances' occurred in abundance some 300 Ma ago when vast swamps blanketed large parts of the Earth. Trees that lived there died and fell into the swamps. Because there was no oxygen to decompose them, they remained, were preserved, and became buried by more and more organic material. Eventually these organic soils were lithified, forming coal and other rocks containing organic carbon (Figure 8.7, arrow M). We burn these ancient trees as coal, and release the energy stored by photosynthesis millions of years ago. Today, there is less vegetation on the Earth's surface, and fewer swamps, so organic matter is transferred at a far lower rate to this long-term reservoir. However, the process still removes about 0.05×10^{12} kg C y^{-1} from the biological carbon cycle.

The total rock reservoir

Over the Earth as a whole, there is approximately four times as much carbonate rock as organic sedimentary rock. Collectively, these rocks are the largest and longest-term reservoir of carbon (Table 8.1). Carbonate rocks store about 40 million $\times 10^{12}$ kg C, by far the largest reservoir of carbon on Earth. Organic sedimentary rocks store about 10 million $\times 10^{12}$ kg C, but only about a thousandth of this is in fossil fuel composed of organic matter (coal, petroleum, natural gas) that is concentrated enough to be usable as a fuel source. However, compared with some other reservoirs — such as the atmosphere, living things or the ocean — this is still a very large reservoir of carbon.

8.6 Return to the biological cycle

You may think that being in rock buried a kilometre or more underground would seal a permanent fate for carbon. But on Earth, nothing is permanent and we will consider here the final steps in completing the global carbon cycle.

8.6.1 Uplifting and weathering

Geological processes, particularly mountain-building, may bring the deeply buried organic and carbonate sedimentary rocks to the surface. The process of uplifting — pushing deeply buried rocks to the surface during movements of the Earth — occurs over time-spans of tens of millions of years, but the net effect, in places such as the Himalayan mountain chain, can be spectacular. You will encounter these processes in detail in Block 3. Here, we are more concerned with the consequences for the carbon cycle.

Carbonate rocks that were long ago part of sediment in an ocean or shallow sea are very common in some areas of the world; they make up limestone or chalky cliffs (such as the white cliffs of Dover), many mountains, and chalky or limestone soils (Figure 8.8). The carbonate rocks we quarry today are the fossilized remains of organisms, mainly plankton or corals, that lived millions of years ago. Coal, too, is mined from deposits that either have been exposed at the surface or lie near the

Figure 8.8 A hillside in west Cyprus, formed of limestones 9 Ma old. These are the fossilized remains of coral reefs that grew in a shallow sea. The pale soils in the foreground are typical of those that develop on limestone rocks.

surface. These were also pushed up from deposits buried kilometres below the surface by movements of the Earth over geological time. The overlying rocks are worn away, exposing these once deeply buried deposits.

Once exposed at the surface, rocks can be weathered. **Weathering** is the gradual disintegration of rock by wind, water or biological activity. Along with other elements, carbon stored in the rock is released, mainly into water (sometimes directly to the air), and thus returns to the biological carbon cycle.

Dissolved in water, carbon weathered from rocks makes up the dissolved carbon of streams and lakes. ('Hard water', containing high levels of dissolved carbon, is characteristic of regions with limestone — the next time you scrape limescale, think of the carbon that may have recently been liberated from hundreds of millions of years trapped in a limestone rock — now solidified again in your kettle!) Rivers transport this dissolved carbon to the surface ocean (Figure 8.7, arrow N). Therefore, although they are only a minor source of dissolved carbon to the surface ocean — about $0.2 \times 10^{12}\,\mathrm{kg\,C\,y^{-1}}$ — rivers are vital to the global carbon cycle because they directly link the geochemical and biological cycles.

8.6.2 Volcanoes

The other major way in which carbon stored in rock can be returned to the biological carbon cycle is through the melting of rock and direct release of carbon to the atmosphere. This occurs primarily in volcanoes, where molten rock from the Earth's interior escapes through cracks and fissures in the Earth's crust to erupt on the surface. When rocks containing carbon, either as carbonate or organic carbon, are melted, gases such as carbon dioxide and water vapour are released (Figure 8.7, arrow O). Again, the carbon that was stored in rock is returned to the biological carbon cycle, this time directly as atmospheric CO_2.

Activity 8.2   Flow diagram of the global carbon cycle: Part IV

In Part IV of this activity, you will complete the seven-box description of the global carbon cycle. ◄

There are no known *natural* processes that could cause such a dramatic increase in atmospheric CO_2 over such a short time. However, the industrial revolution, which involved a huge increase in the use of coal as a source of energy, got underway in Europe during the 18th century. Economies all over the world have become more and more industrialized since then, consuming ever-increasing amounts of fossil fuel (petroleum and gas, as well as coal). A second human influence is deforestation. Recall from Section 8.4.1 that one consequence of converting large areas of tropical rain forest into agricultural land is that less carbon is stored in biomass. When this wood is burned, as is usually the case, the carbon in the wood becomes CO_2 in the atmosphere. The rate of deforestation, especially in the tropics, has increased dramatically in recent decades.

Thus, the amount of CO_2 in the atmosphere has increased along with the increased consumption of fossil fuel and increased clearance of tropical forests. Many people are convinced that this is far more than a coincidence.

The 1990s rate at which carbon is being put into the atmosphere by human activity is known to a reasonable degree of accuracy: a total of about 7×10^{12} kg C y^{-1}. Fossil-fuel burning accounts for 5.4×10^{12} kg C y^{-1} (a value known to a high degree of accuracy), and the clearing and burning of forests for the rest (a value not as accurately known, but thought to be in the range of $1-2 \times 10^{12}$ kg C y^{-1}).

○ The carbon released from fossil-fuel burning is a direct release from the rock reservoir (organic sedimentary rock) to the atmosphere reservoir. Use Figure 8.7 to determine how the rate of this process compares with the natural rates of transfer of carbon from the rock reservoir.

○ Carbon is transferred from the rock reservoir by weathering (arrow N) and volcanism (arrow O). These release 0.2×10^{12} kg C y^{-1} and 0.05×10^{12} kg C y^{-1} respectively, giving a total of 0.25×10^{12} kg C y^{-1}. The release from fossil-fuel burning is 5.4×10^{12} kg C y^{-1}, which is about 20 times faster than natural processes.

8.7.2 Where is it going?

The atmosphere reservoir is small — it contains only about 760×10^{12} kg C (Table 8.1). Therefore, even small releases from the fossil fuel (rock) and forest (living things) reservoirs cause significant increases in the atmospheric reservoir (see Question 8.1). An annual addition of 7×10^{12} kg of carbon to the atmosphere would mean an increase of nearly 1% per year.

Activity 8.4   Calculating increases in atmospheric CO_2

In this activity you will compare the *observed* annual increase in atmospheric CO_2 with the rate of release of CO_2 to the atmosphere each year by the human activities of fossil-fuel burning and deforestation. ◀

Activity 8.4 should have told you that not all of the carbon put into the atmosphere by human activity (about 7×10^{12} kg C y^{-1}) is accumulating in the atmosphere. In fact, only about 40% of it is — about 3×10^{12} kg C y^{-1}. Current estimates suggest that an additional 2×10^{12} kg C y^{-1} are probably dissolving in the surface ocean. The fate of the 'missing' $1-2 \times 10^{12}$ kg C y^{-1} has been vigorously debated for years, but it seems increasingly likely that it is being temporarily stored in vegetation in the Northern Hemisphere through increased production and growth of trees. No one knows how long this uptake, if indeed it is occurring at all, will continue.

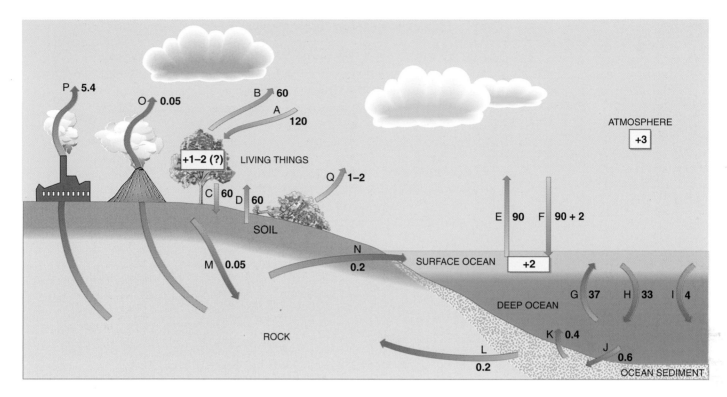

Figure 8.11 gives our final version of the carbon cycle — the modern one. Note the two new human-caused releases of carbon into the atmosphere: arrow P, which shows the burning of fossil fuels as an extra transfer process from rock to the atmosphere; and arrow Q, which shows the clearing and burning of forests as an extra transfer process from living things to the atmosphere. The resulting annual increases in the reservoirs of carbon in the atmosphere, surface ocean, and living things are shown in boxes. The largest change has been in the atmosphere — the 1996 level of about 760×10^{12} kg C (Table 8.1) was about 30% higher than the 'pre-industrial' level of about 590×10^{12} kg C estimated from ice-cores.

Carbon dioxide is a greenhouse gas, and the effect on the GMST of the increase in atmospheric CO_2 will be taken up in Section 10, where we will also look to the future. Before that, in the next section, we will see if we can understand climate changes in the recent and distant past, and this will involve looking at factors additional to CO_2. This attempt to explain the past should help scientists to predict the future.

Now that you have made a full trip around the global carbon cycle, you are ready to explore it more fully in Activity 8.5.

Activity 8.5   An element on the move

In this first CD-ROM activity of the course, 'An element on the move', you will 'be' a carbon atom, and will move through and explore an expanded number of reservoirs in a sequence of your own choosing. Remember that important notes for this activity can be found in the Study File. ◀

Figure 8.11 A pictorial representation of today's carbon cycle — rates of input and output do not balance, and some reservoirs (atmosphere, surface ocean, living things) are not in a steady state. Estimated annual changes in the sizes of these reservoirs are shown in boxes. The rates P and Q represent human-accelerated release of carbon from the rock reservoir to the atmosphere (P) and from the living things reservoir to the atmosphere (Q). Rate F has increased by about 2×10^{12} kg C y^{-1}.

8.8   Summary of Section 8

The Earth's surface temperature is determined in part by the amount of the greenhouse gas CO_2 in the atmosphere. Without the infrared absorption provided by CO_2 the Earth's surface would be much cooler.

The amount of CO_2 in the atmosphere is controlled by the global carbon cycle. This cycle, which is summarized in Figure 8.11, describes the movement and major transformations of carbon on Earth.

The global carbon cycle can be broken down into a biological cycle, where carbon moves fairly rapidly through the atmosphere, living things, soil and surface ocean (time-scales of years to tens of years), and a geochemical cycle, where carbon moves slowly through the deep ocean, sediment and rock (time-scales of thousands to millions of years).

The atmosphere is a relatively small reservoir of carbon (mostly CO_2) with direct links to all of the other reservoirs of the biological cycle and, importantly, to the rock reservoir of the geochemical cycle. Therefore, small changes in either biological or geochemical reservoirs of carbon can have a large effect on the atmospheric content of CO_2. Through the greenhouse effect, this in turn might affect climate. Climate, then, is intimately linked with the living things on Earth and with the geological activities of rock formation, mountain building and volcanic activity.

By burning fossil fuels, humans have accelerated, by about 20 times, the rate of release of carbon stored in the rock reservoir. Deforestation has increased the rate of release of carbon from the living things reservoir. There is no doubt that there has been a significant increase in the amount of CO_2 in the atmosphere as a result.

Can we explain past variations in the GMST?

You have now studied a wide range of science related to the GMST, much of it at a detailed level. In this section we return to the broad picture, but first Activity 9.1 gives you the valuable opportunity to take stock of what has been covered up to now.

Activity 9.1   Writing a brief summary of earlier sections

In this activity, you are asked to encapsulate the central message of each of Sections 1 to 8 in a sentence or two. ◀

In Section 1 we established that variations in the GMST of just a few degrees Celsius could have significant consequences for human life and for life in general. In Sections 2 and 3 we saw that the GMST has indeed varied in the past, part of the evidence being the significant effect that these variations have had on living things. The factors that determine the GMST were the subject of Sections 4 and 5, and these include the atmospheric constituents that give rise to the Earth's greenhouse effect. Our examination of the Earth's atmosphere in Section 6 identified water vapour and carbon dioxide as the major greenhouse gases. In Sections 7 and 8, respectively, we discussed the cycles that determine the amounts of water vapour and carbon dioxide in the atmosphere. Though there are stabilizing mechanisms, these amounts can change significantly, and therefore so can the GMST.

The time has now come to broaden the picture again, and to consider the effect on the GMST of changing not only the atmospheric amounts of water vapour and carbon dioxide, but also the other factors that we identified earlier. Moreover, we want *numbers* — we want to know by how much the GMST might vary when a factor changes by a certain amount. In this section you will have the opportunity to calculate the variations in the GMST when one or more factors are changed by amounts that you specify.

Mathematical models of the Earth's climate system

In order to calculate the actual amount by which the GMST varies when one or more factors are changed by specific amounts, we need a mathematical model of the Earth's climate system. A **mathematical model** consists of a set of equations, each of which calculates one quantity from other quantities. You have met several equations in this block. For example, in Section 2 you met the equation for calculating the GMST from a global set of mean surface temperatures.

⬤ What was this equation?

◯ $$\text{GMST} = \frac{\text{sum of all mean surface temperatures}}{\text{number of surface locations}} \tag{2.3}$$

In a mathematical **climate model** there are a large number of equations. For example, there will be one for calculating the rate at which solar radiation is absorbed by the Earth's surface, and another for calculating the rate at which infrared radiation is emitted by the surface. Moreover, for calculating the GMST, rather than treating the atmosphere as a single entity as we did in Section 5, it is better to divide it into horizontal layers, with energy transfers by convection, latent heat, and radiation between one layer and the others. More equations will be needed to calculate these transfers.

A complication is that the equations are not independent of each other. For example, if there is a change in the rate at which solar radiation is absorbed by the Earth's surface, then there will be a consequent change in the rate at which infrared radiation is emitted by the surface. This interaction between equations is called *coupling*. Indeed, each equation is coupled to almost all of the other equations, and so we not only have a large number of equations in the climate model, but also a large measure of coupling. Coupling can lead to feedback (Section 7.5).

One outcome of working through the set of equations in a climate model will be a value of the GMST. In a complex model the number of (coupled) equations will be so large that it is not feasible to do the calculations by hand or with a pocket calculator; it would take a very long time indeed to calculate the GMST. Therefore, the calculations are done with the aid of a computer. A mathematical model on a computer is often called a **computer model**.

Various climate models have been developed to calculate the GMST, and there are others that additionally calculate *regional* surface temperatures. The variety arises from the complexity of the Earth's climate system, and no mathematical model yet includes all the details. This is partly because the more detailed the model the longer the computing time to produce results, resulting in huge expense, and it is partly because some of the equations are not known, or known only approximately. For example, the equations that calculate the amount of cloud cover are particularly uncertain. Consequently, the results from all models are uncertain to some degree. Different models are constructed to be good at calculating different things; you will see examples of the results from different models in Sections 9.1 and 9.2 and Section 10.

In Section 9.1 you will be introduced to the computer models included in the CD-ROM activity 'Global warming and cooling'. After you have worked with 'Global warming and cooling' you will then, in Section 9.2, address the vital question of whether climate models can explain past changes in the GMST: *this is the main objective of this section.*

9.1 Global warming and cooling

Before you work with 'Global warming and cooling' you need to know something about the climate models it contains.

9.1.1 Preparation for 'Global warming and cooling'

The first climate model in 'Global warming and cooling' calculates the GMST. In broad terms, this model consists of equations for calculating the GMST from all the various globally averaged energy gains and losses in Figure 5.14, though in the computer model the atmosphere is divided into several horizontal layers. In spite of this important refinement, there are no types of energy gain and loss that you have not already met.

Question 9.1   One energy gain is solar radiation absorbed by the Earth's atmosphere, and one loss is convection from the Earth's surface. List four of the other surface or atmospheric energy gains and losses that determine the GMST. ◄

The energy gains and losses depend on the solar constant (Section 5.1), and on various properties of the Earth's atmosphere and surface. Those properties that are subject to significant change in the real world are listed in Table 9.1. In 'Global warming and cooling' you will not be able to change all of these properties — that would be too complex a task — but you will be able to change most of them.

Table 9.1   The main atmospheric and surface properties that determine the GMST, and that are subject to significant change in the real world.

Atmospheric properties that affect solar radiation	Atmospheric properties that affect longwave infrared radiation	Surface properties that affect solar radiation
clouds: cover, type, altitude, thickness	clouds: cover, type, altitude, thickness	albedo of surfaces free of ice and snow
aerosols: content, type, altitude	aerosols: content, type, altitude	fraction of surface covered by ice and snow
	amount of greenhouse gases (CO_2, H_2O, etc.)	

Table 9.1 goes a little beyond our earlier discussion, and so we need to consider briefly the entries in the table, starting with clouds. Clouds affect solar radiation through their contribution to the planetary albedo.

What is the planetary albedo?

It is the fraction of the solar radiation intercepted by the Earth that is scattered and reflected back to space by the atmosphere and the surface (Section 5.1.1).

Clouds also affect longwave infrared radiation. They absorb radiation, and consequently they increase the amount of infrared radiation emitted by the atmosphere. The effects of clouds depend on the fraction of the Earth's surface covered in cloud — the cloud cover — and also on the altitude of the clouds, their thickness, and their type. The type is determined by the details of the liquid or solid water particles that make up the cloud.

Other atmospheric aerosols also contribute to the planetary albedo and to the absorption and emission of longwave infrared radiation. Note that in Table 9.1 we have followed common practice and listed these other aerosols separately from clouds. Their effect on the planetary albedo and their effect on longwave infrared radiation depend on the size of the particles, their composition, and their location in the atmosphere. Aerosols are produced in many and varied ways, including through human activity. Sometimes the aerosol is released as particles, for example smoke and dust, and sometimes the particles form as a result of chemical reactions between atmospheric constituents and emitted gases, for example from volcanoes or power stations. In the troposphere (Section 6.2) the residence time is short, partly because aerosols act as condensation nuclei for cloud formation, and thus are removed by precipitation. In the stratosphere (Section 6.2), which is largely free from clouds, the residence time is several years. Aerosols throughout the atmosphere are only roughly in a steady state, and, apart from human activity, volcanoes are an important disturbance. A major volcanic eruption can give rise to a sufficient increase in stratospheric aerosols to have noticeable, if short-term, effects on global climate.

Surface properties are listed in Table 9.1 as affecting only solar radiation. This is because the surface properties that affect the absorption and emission of longwave infrared radiation are not subject to significant change in the real world. By contrast, surface properties that influence solar radiation *are* subject to significant change. It is the contribution that the surface makes to the planetary albedo that is important. A useful simple subdivision is to separate the Earth's surface into the fraction that is covered in ice and snow, and the rest, which includes the oceans and a variety of landscapes. The rest has an overall albedo defined as the fraction of the solar radiation incident on the surface free of ice and snow that is reflected. The albedo of ice and snow shows little variation as a global average, and so this albedo is not included in the table.

The second model in 'Global warming and cooling' will allow you to explore something we have so far paid only scant attention to in this block, namely the mean surface temperatures at *different places* on the Earth's surface. Remember that the GMST is the mean temperature over the *whole* surface of the Earth. At a particular location or region, the mean temperature is called simply the mean surface temperature, MST. Obviously, the MST is not the same everywhere: for example, it is lower in polar regions than in equatorial regions. Not obvious at all is that a given change in GMST will lead to larger changes in the MST in some places, and smaller changes in others. The second model allows you to explore these regional differences. In place of the globally averaged picture of Figure 5.14, the Earth in the model is divided into a number of separate locations that interact with each other.

In order to explore the changes in the MST in different regions you have to be familiar with how a location on the Earth's surface is specified. This is done by specifying the latitude and longitude of the location, terms that are explained in Box 9.1, *Latitude, longitude and angles*.

Box 9.1   Latitude, longitude and angles

A smooth ball, such as the billiard ball in Figure 9.1a, is a good model of the shape of the Earth. To understand latitude and longitude you must first realize that the Earth rotates (once a day). We can use the ball to demonstrate this rotation by spinning it (Figure 9.1a). Figure 9.1b shows that the ball is rotating around an imaginary line through its centre. This is called the **axis of rotation**, or rotation axis. This axis crosses the surface of the ball at two points, which are called the poles of the axis. In the case of the Earth the poles are called the North Pole and the South Pole. The imaginary line around the Earth half-way between the poles is called the Equator (Figure 9.1c).

A large ball with a map of the Earth painted on it is a geographical globe, and Figure 9.2 shows such a globe from two viewpoints. This globe is marked with two sets of lines on its surface that enable us to specify a surface location. In Figure 9.2a the blue lines running from left to right are lines of **latitude**, the Equator being one such line, and the red lines running from one pole to the other are lines of **longitude**. In Figure 9.2b, which is the view from above the North Pole, the circles are the lines of latitude and the lines radiating out from the pole are the lines of longitude. Lines of longitude are semicircles, as you can see in Figure 9.2a. Lines of longitude are all the same length, unlike the lines of latitude which become smaller circles the nearer they are to a pole, and are points at the poles themselves.

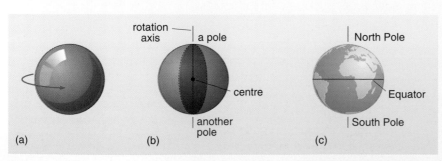

Figure 9.1   (a) A smooth ball representing the shape of the Earth. The ball is spinning to represent the Earth's rotation. (b) A cutaway showing the axis of rotation of the ball, which goes through its centre and emerges at points on its surface called poles. (c) The poles and the Equator of the Earth.

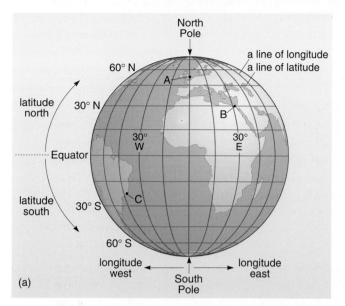

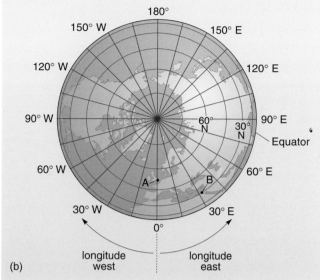

Figure 9.2   A geographical globe (a) viewed from above the Equator, (b) viewed from above the North Pole. Lines of latitude and longitude are shown at 15° intervals.

The unit of measurement for latitude and longitude is the degree. This is a general unit for measuring angles. An **angle** is the amount of 'turn' between one direction and another, and Figure 9.3 shows some examples of angles in terms of the difference in direction between two lines that meet. The unit of angle is the degree of arc, usually just called the **degree**, symbol °. It is nothing whatsoever to do with the degree Celsius, which, as you know, is a measure of temperature.

Note that the angle between two directions that are the same is zero. Consider now the angle between two directions that are perpendicular to each other (Figure 9.3c). Regardless of the unit we are using, this angle is called a **right angle**. In degrees, a right

angle has the value 90°, which raises the question of why it couldn't have been 100°, or some other round number. The 90° convention has come to us from earlier civilizations, notably from the Babylonians who flourished in the Middle East in the first and second millennia BC. They had a good reason to define the degree as they did, which we can see if we note from Figure 9.3g that the angle in a complete turn is 360°. This is not very different from the number of days in the year (365), and it seems likely that this is the basis of the choice in those far-off days of 360° for a complete turn.

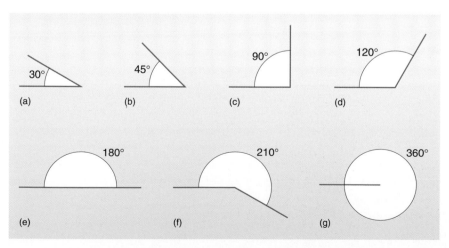

Figure 9.3   Some angles, measured in degrees. Note the way in which the angles are marked and labelled.

141

⬤ What is the angle in degrees between one direction and the opposite direction?

◐ This is two right angles, 180°, as in Figure 9.3e.

A useful device for measuring angles on a diagram is a protractor, such as that shown in Figure 9.4. The baseline of the protractor is placed on one of the two lines as shown, and the angle is read off from where the other line intersects the scale on the semicircular edge of the protractor.

That lines of longitude can be measured in degrees is clear from Figure 9.2b, where the lines radiate out from the pole. One line is chosen as 0° and the other lines are at angles that increase to the west and to the east. You can see that 180° W (west) and 180° E (east) are the same, half-way around the globe from 0°. The position of the 0° line has to be decided, and by international agreement it is the line that passes through the old Greenwich Observatory in London, marked A in Figure 9.2. This zero of longitude is called the Greenwich Meridian.

That lines of latitude can be measured in degrees is apparent from Figure 9.5, which is derived from Figure 9.2a by cutting a segment out of the model Earth. The Equator is chosen as 0°, and as we go towards the North Pole the latitude increases, to reach 90° N at the pole itself. South of the Equator the latitude again increases, to reach 90° S at the South Pole.

◑ Use Figure 9.2 to specify to the nearest 5° the latitude and longitude of London (A), Cairo (B) and Rio de Janeiro (C).

◐ London: just over 50° N, about 0° longitude. Cairo: about 30° N, just over 30° E. Rio de Janeiro: about 23° S, just under 45° W.

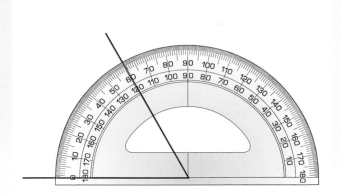

Figure 9.4 A protractor being used to measure an angle, in this case 60°.

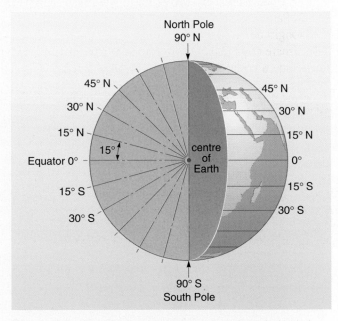

Figure 9.5 The Earth, cut away to show how latitude is measured in degrees.

The spinning ball and the geographical globe used in Box 9.1 are examples of a type of model called a scale model. In a **scale model** the model is a different size from the object being modelled and it might be made of different materials. A model railway is a familiar example. The ball and globe are certainly very much smaller than the Earth and are also made of different materials, but they model effectively the property of the Earth of interest, its shape. They are examples of spheres, and the Earth is very nearly a sphere. Of course, the scale model doesn't have all the fine detail of surface shape on the Earth, but this does not matter. However, all its dimensions are in a constant ratio to the dimensions of the real Earth.

A scale model need not be static. Model railways imitate the motion of real trains, and the spin of the globe or ball imitates the rotation of the Earth. As with all types of model, scale models are simplified representations of the real world. They aid understanding by focusing on some particular aspects of reality. Thus the ball and globe focus on the general shape and rotation of the Earth, and ignore other aspects, such as the interior structure of the Earth.

Activity 9.2   Global warming and cooling

You should now work with the CD-ROM activity 'Global warming and cooling'. ◀

9.1.2   Some reflections on 'Global warming and cooling'

In 'Global warming and cooling' the two climate models are simplified in several ways in order that they can be used to calculate new temperatures in a reasonable amount of computing time. One obvious simplification in the second model is that the Earth's surface properties are assumed to have no variation with longitude. Consequently, it is only possible to calculate the MST at different latitudes. In reality, the Earth's surface properties vary greatly with longitude. For example, if we journey west at the latitude of London we leave the rolling landscape of the UK, then cross the Atlantic Ocean, then Canada with its central plains and huge mountain ranges, then the north Pacific Ocean, and so on. These longitude variations in the Earth's surface lead to longitude variations in climate at a fixed latitude. There is a direct effect, in which climate at a fixed latitude varies with surface altitude and with distance from the sea, and an indirect effect through the influence of winds and ocean currents.

There is no doubt that, in general, the more elaborate the model the more confidence we should be able to have in its results: the Earth's climate system is so complicated that simple models are well known to give inferior results. Though the climate models in 'Global warming and cooling' are not particularly simple, far more elaborate models exist. You might therefore expect that the uncertainties in the predictions of these more elaborate models would be smaller: unfortunately, such is our present ignorance of some of the processes that are of importance to climate, the uncertainties are comparable. When a factor is changed by a certain amount, the calculated temperature changes might, for all we know, be two or perhaps even three times different from the changes that would occur in reality.

This might seem disappointing. It is less disappointing when you realize that without even a simple model you would not have known whether, for example, an increase in atmospheric CO_2 by 10% would lead to an increase in GMST by 0.01 °C, or 0.1 °C, or 1 °C, or some other wildly different value.

But of course we do want values that are as realistic as possible. So, how successful are the most elaborate climate models in explaining the past changes in the GMST? Furthermore, can such models predict regional and seasonal temperatures?

9.2   Can we explain past climates?

Even in the most elaborate models there is a significant degree of simplification compared with the real Earth. Moreover, some of the important processes are too poorly understood to be modelled properly, particularly cloud formation. Additionally, as we go further into the past we are less certain of the climates that prevailed, and of many of the important factors that determine the climate, such as the solar constant and atmospheric composition. Different teams of modellers come up with different compromises, and therefore there is more than one model and more than one set of conclusions!

In general, the calculated values of the GMST are more reliable than those of regional temperatures and of other features of climate such as precipitation. In any case it is with the GMST that this block is mainly concerned, and therefore it is only the explanations of past changes in GMST that we shall consider here.

9.2.1   Why has the GMST varied over the past few thousand years?

In Section 3 you saw that we are currently in an interglacial period that started about 10 000 years ago. Detailed studies show that since then the GMST has varied by up to about a degree Celsius, with the warmer and cooler periods persisting for hundreds of years. What explanations do the best models offer for these relatively short-term, relatively modest variations in GMST?

A plausible explanation, though at present difficult to prove, is that the Sun is an important contributor to the variation in GMST over this comparatively recent period. In particular, the solar 'constant' has varied!

● What is the solar constant?

○ It is the amount of solar radiation falling on a square metre facing the Sun just above the Earth's atmosphere, averaged over a few years (Section 5.1).

Accurate measurements of the solar constant extend back for only a couple of decades, but there is indirect evidence that the solar constant varies by up to about 0.5% on a time-scale of a few decades, i.e. the average over a few decades can differ by up to about 0.5% compared with the average over the preceding or succeeding few decades. The solar constant depends on the solar luminosity.

● What is the solar luminosity?

○ It is the total power in the electromagnetic radiation from the Sun (Section 5.1).

In addition to the solar luminosity, the solar constant also depends on the distance of the Earth from the Sun. If the Sun were farther away but had the same luminosity the solar constant would be smaller, just as the heating effect of a fire diminishes with distance. However, the average distance of the Earth from the Sun does not change significantly, and so changes in the solar constant are a consequence of changes in the solar luminosity.

> From about 1600 to about 1850, a combination of changes in the solar constant and variations in volcanic aerosols seems able to account for the variations in the GMST. Since 1850, human-generated greenhouse gases, particularly CO_2, have become increasingly important.

Human activities have raised the CO_2 level from about 285 p.p.m. in 1850 to about 360 p.p.m. in 1996, and this is probably the biggest single cause of the 0.7 °C or so rise in GMST since 1850 (Figure 2.13).

Before about 1600 the picture becomes less clear the further we go into the past, with climate data, and data on the solar constant and other factors, being less reliable.

> It is *plausible* that the GMST variations throughout the current interglacial period are due to a combination of changes in the solar constant and variations in volcanic aerosols, but climatologists cannot yet be certain that other factors have not been important.

Note that a small change in some factor might not in itself be sufficient to account for the whole of a particular change in the GMST, but it could nevertheless have been the primary cause of the whole change. This is because the effect of the small change can be amplified by positive feedback (Section 7.5), and because of coupling between factors. Positive feedback (and negative feedback) and coupling make it even more difficult to be certain of the primary cause(s) of a change in GMST.

Question 9.2 A decrease in the solar constant would be expected to lead to an increase in the fraction of the Earth's surface covered by snow and ice. Explain how the immediate effect on the GMST leads to an example of positive feedback. ◄

9.2.2 Why has the GMST varied in the more distant past?

You saw in Sections 3.2 and 3.3 that the GMST has varied considerably on huge time-scales throughout the 4 600 Ma of Earth history. Can these long-term variations also be explained by climate models? To a limited extent they can. The explanations include some combination of four contributory factors, plus the effects of feedback. We will conclude this section with an outline of the four factors and with a broad indication of how they help to account for the long-term variations in the GMST. Note that we are *not* concerned here with the short-term variations in the GMST that presumably have also occurred, in part as a result of the short-term changes in solar luminosity and volcanic aerosols discussed in the previous section.

Changes in the Earth's orbit and in the tilt of its rotation axis

For the past few million years the main cause of long-term variations in the GMST has probably been the combined effect of changes in the Earth's **orbit** around the Sun and in the tilt of its rotation axis — its **axial tilt**. Consider the orbital changes first. The Earth goes around the Sun once a year in an orbit that appears circular, with the Sun at the centre. In fact, the shape of the orbit is not quite circular and it varies very slightly over 93 000 years in a repeating cycle. At the scale of this page the variation is not noticeable, so in Figure 9.6 we have greatly exaggerated it. At one extreme the orbit is elongated with the Sun off-centre, and at the opposite extreme the orbit is very nearly circular with the Sun at the centre.

The axial tilt also changes. In 'Global warming and cooling' you saw that the rotation axis of the Earth is tilted with respect to its orbit, as in Figure 9.7a. This shows the Earth (greatly exaggerated in size) in two positions in its orbit, in an oblique view — remember that the orbit is almost circular. The present tilt (23.5°) is shown more clearly in Figure 9.7b along with the maximum and minimum values. This figure is not exaggerated but shows the actual range of tilts.

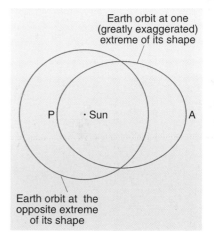

Figure 9.6 The two extremes in the shape of the Earth's orbit.

What is the effect of these orbital and axial tilt changes? The distance of the Earth from the Sun averaged over a complete orbit is not significantly altered by the variation in orbital shape. When the Earth is in the region of P in its elongated orbit (Figure 9.6) it is closer to the Sun than when it is in its circular orbit, whereas in the region of A it is farther from the Sun. So the *average* Earth–Sun distance is not much altered by the slight variations in orbital shape. This distance is not at all altered by the variation in axial tilt (Figure 9.7). Therefore the solar constant is *not* significantly affected by these variations (nor by other, smaller variations in the orbit and axial tilt). Their main effect is to alter the latitudinal and seasonal variations in solar radiation, and this can lead to changes in climate, including changes in the GMST.

One example of how this works will suffice. Consider the variation in the axial tilt, and to make the effect clearer let's suppose that the tilt can vary from zero to far

145

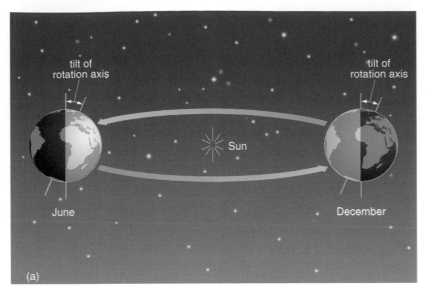

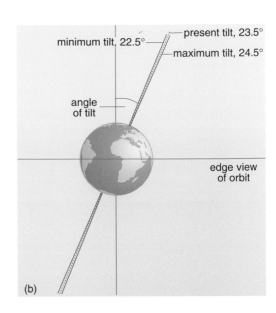

Figure 9.7 (a) The tilt of the Earth's rotation axis at two positions in the Earth's orbit. (b) The range of axial tilts of the Earth (to scale). It takes 41 000 years for the Earth to go from minimum tilt (22.5°) to the maximum (24.5°), and back to the minimum again.

larger than its present value, as in Figure 9.8. When the tilt is zero (Figure 9.8a) the solar radiation at the surface in each polar region is very weak all year round, and the polar regions are therefore always very cold. When the tilt is large (Figure 9.8b) then each polar region receives no solar radiation in its winter, though this is not much less than the tiny amount of radiation it receives all the year at zero tilt. By contrast, each polar region now receives considerable radiation in its summer. Averaged over a year, each pole now receives *more* radiation than it did when the tilt was smaller. This is a bit like receiving an income of £0 in the winter months and £100 in the summer months (large tilt), compared with £5 a month all the year (zero tilt).

The polar regions thus receive more solar radiation on average when the tilt is larger, and this can lead to a retreat of the polar ice-caps. Models show that this leads to a general increase in the GMST. Conversely, when the tilt becomes smaller this can give rise to a growth in the size of the polar ice-caps and to a general decrease in the GMST.

Figure 9.8 (a) Zero tilt of the Earth's axis: the polar regions are always very cold. (b) Large tilt of the Earth's axis: the polar regions are still cold in winter but much warmer in the summer and so, on average, are warmer than when the tilt is zero.

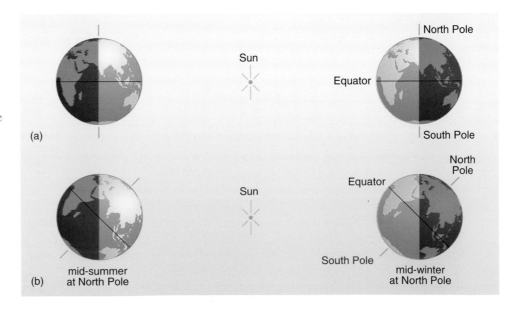

⬤ What positive feedback effect enhances the influence on the GMST of changes in the size of the polar ice-caps?

◯ If there is a greater area of the Earth covered by ice and snow the planetary albedo increases and this leads to further cooling by reflecting back to space a greater fraction of solar radiation (Question 9.2). If a smaller area is covered then the planetary albedo decreases, and this leads to further warming.

This example of changes in axial tilt also illustrates an important general point: in order to calculate a globally averaged quantity, such as the change in the GMST, it is an advantage to model what is happening at different locations. The first model in 'Global warming and cooling' treats the Earth as one big location and ignores any variation from place to place. It thus can't accommodate the orbital and axial changes that we have been discussing, and so the accuracy of the calculated changes in the GMST is reduced.

The combined effects on the GMST of the various changes in the Earth's orbit and axial tilt, aided by positive feedback, have been calculated with the models most suitable for this purpose, for periods of a few million years. The result is that a reasonable match is obtained with the *actual* record of changes in GMST. In particular, there is a good correspondence between the predicted times at which major warmings or coolings should have occurred, and the times when the evidence indicates that they actually occurred. Therefore it seems possible that these changes in orbit and in axial tilt are the primary causes of the recorded *major* changes in GMST over the past few million years.

These orbital and axial tilt changes have been occurring throughout the 4 600 Ma of Earth history, and presumably have played a significant role throughout this time.

Changes in the oceans and continents

Another influence on climate throughout Earth history has been very slow changes in the form of the Earth's surface. As you will see in Block 3, the continents and the oceans of the Earth are not fixed in area or in position. This means that the distribution of land and sea over the globe has changed, as have the heights of mountain ranges and the shapes of the ocean floors. All these things influence the Earth's climate through their effect on the variations of albedo with latitude and longitude, and on the winds and ocean currents. Scientists know reasonably well how the continents and oceans have evolved over the past few hundred millions of years, so this is built into models of this period to help account for changes in GMST. Further back in time our knowledge is less certain.

Long-term changes in solar luminosity

Yet another influence on climate throughout Earth history has been long-term changes in solar luminosity. It is believed from astronomical evidence that the Sun's luminosity 4 600 Ma ago was only about 70% of its present value. Since then it has increased fairly steadily, though there must have been some irregularities. Figure 9.9 shows a plausible general trend. Note that the 10 000 years of the present interglacial period is too short an interval to show on this figure!

⬤ The average distance of the Earth from the Sun has changed negligibly throughout Earth history, so what can we conclude from Figure 9.9 about the solar constant?

◯ The solar constant has also increased from 70% of its present value.

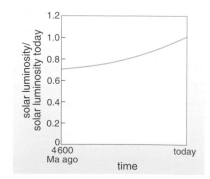

Figure 9.9 A plausible variation in solar luminosity since the Earth was born 4 600 Ma ago.

'Global warming and cooling' showed you how sensitive the GMST is to the solar constant. Working backwards, the GMST with the solar constant at 70% of its present value would have been low enough for the whole Earth to be covered in ice, and it would have been at least many hundreds of millions of years before the solar constant rose to the point where the ice melted. There is geological evidence that the Earth was *not* completely ice-covered throughout its early history. Thus there must have been compensating effects, and one possibility is that the composition of the atmosphere was very different.

Changes in atmospheric composition

This is the last of the four factors that together enable us to explain to a reasonable extent the long-term variations in the GMST.

Ever since the Earth was born the composition of the atmosphere has changed. For example, periods of enhanced volcanic activity have led to an increase in the aerosol content. There might also have been short periods when the aerosol content increased hugely as a result of bodies several kilometres across hitting the Earth from space. Though aerosols are washed from the atmosphere in a few years, an unusually large amount can cause longer-lasting effects by triggering a climate change that outlives the aerosol itself. Unfortunately, whether an aerosol tends to increase or decrease the GMST depends on the type of aerosol, and on its location in the atmosphere. Therefore, a greater aerosol content early in Earth history would not necessarily have helped to compensate for low solar luminosity.

Reduced cloud cover would have helped, because the dominant effect of a reduction is to reduce the planetary albedo. It is *possible* that there was less cloud cover throughout much of early Earth history, though there is much uncertainty about this. Greater amounts of greenhouse gases would also have helped to compensate for the low solar luminosity. In Section 8 you saw the various factors that determine the atmospheric amount of the greenhouse gas CO_2.

● Why might there have been more CO_2 in the atmosphere early in Earth history than there is today?

○ This would have been largely because the oceans had not yet had time to remove most of the CO_2 in the formation of carbonates and rocks rich in organic carbon (Section 8.5.3). Also, the biomass would have been smaller.

The current view is that early in Earth history there was many times the present amount of CO_2 in the atmosphere. This, combined with less cloud cover, is a plausible way to offset the low solar luminosity, thus preventing the Earth from being frozen throughout much of its youth. On this view, as the solar luminosity gradually rose, the GMST was stabilized by an increase in the cloud cover, and geological processes that reduced the atmospheric CO_2 content.

This makes a nice link with the most recent past, the last hundred years or so, where CO_2 has again become an important factor in climate change, and it makes a nice link with Section 10, where the role of CO_2 in the near future is a central element of the story.

We conclude this section with a caution. At present our knowledge of past conditions, and our understanding of the Earth's climate system, are too poor for us to be *certain* that we understand the causes of temperature changes in the past, particularly in the distant past. Bear this in mind in Section 10.

Activity 9.3   The effect on the GMST of dust in space

Though there is no definite evidence for it, it is plausible that the amount of dust between the Earth and the Sun has varied throughout Earth history. This activity asks you to consider the effect on the GMST of an increase in this amount of dust. ◀

Activity 9.4   Variations in the GMST versus changes in various factors

This activity gives you practice at summarizing, and also allows you to draw together some of the material in this section. ◀

Activity 9.5   Models in science

This activity is intended to help you develop your understanding of the use of models in science. ◀

9.3   Summary of Section 9

The two climate models in 'Global warming and cooling' are adequate for showing the general way in which the Earth's surface temperature depends on the solar constant, and on various properties of the Earth's atmosphere and surface.

The best climate models provide widely accepted explanations of much of the variation in the GMST over the past few hundred years, and have identified plausible causes of the variation throughout the 10 000 years of the current interglacial period. Variations in the solar constant of up to about 0.5%, and variations in volcanic aerosols seem to be the main factors, with the effect of the release of CO_2 by human activities becoming significant in the past 100 years or so.

Over the past few million years the main trigger of changes in the GMST seems to have been changes in the Earth's orbit around the Sun and in the tilt of its rotation axis. These changes have altered the latitudinal and seasonal distribution of solar radiation.

On a longer time-scale, extending over the whole of the 4 600 Ma history of the Earth, additional factors become important, in particular:

*   the areas, positions and shapes of oceans and continents;
*   the long-term increase in solar luminosity;
*   variations in atmospheric composition.

Our detailed understanding of changes in the GMST for all but the last few centuries is rather poor because:

*   the Earth's climate system is very complicated; attempts to model it are hindered by lack of knowledge about important processes, and by the many couplings between one effect and others leading to a variety of possible feedback processes (positive and negative);
*   many of the factors that determine the climate are poorly known for the distant past, as indeed are the climates themselves.

10 The Earth's temperature in the future

In this section we shall consider predicted changes in the GMST over various future time-scales, as well as some of the possible consequences of these changes. Obviously such an enterprise is somewhat risky. Danish Nobel Prize-winning physicist Niels Bohr (1885–1962) is said to have warned that 'prediction is very difficult — especially about the future'! Nevertheless, the possible consequences of even quite modest changes in the GMST are so far-reaching (Section 1) that science *must* play its role in our preparations to cope with them. In projecting the 'story' of the Earth's temperature into the future, we'll also revise some of the science introduced in earlier sections.

The present value of the GMST is about 15 °C. However, we know that it has sometimes been higher, and sometimes lower, than this in the past (Sections 2 and 3). Although it's *possible* that the Earth finally emerged from its latest ice age about 10 000 years ago, it's rather more likely that we're now in a relatively brief interglacial period. Many such periods have occurred since the start of the most recent ice age about 2.4 Ma ago. Ice ages themselves usually last several tens of millions of years. Over the past 2 300 Ma they seem to have recurred fairly regularly (Figure 3.16).

○ On the basis of this brief overview of ice ages, and information from Sections 2 and 3, what predictions can you make about likely future levels of the GMST?

○ The most obvious prediction is that the GMST is likely to change in the future — if only because it has done so in the past. A second, more specific, prediction is that the GMST is likely to fall sometime over the next few thousand or tens of thousands of years as the current interglacial period comes to an end. A third prediction is that, eventually, the GMST is likely to rise again — both during any future interglacial periods within the current ice age and when the ice age finally comes to an end. Lastly, there will probably be future ice ages with their glacial and interglacial periods.

In considering possible future changes in the GMST, we obviously need to specify the time-scale we have in mind. This section deals mainly with possible changes in the GMST to the year 2100, i.e. over the time-scale of most concern to the present and next few human generations. In Section 10.2 we'll look at how the GMST might change over this period and in Section 10.3 at some possible consequences of these changes. Finally, in Section 10.4, we'll look at some predictions that have been made for the Earth's climate beyond 2100. However, we'll first revise some earlier material to help you to follow the later arguments.

10.1 The GMST and atmospheric CO_2

As a consequence of the Earth's natural greenhouse effect, the GMST is presently considerably higher than it would otherwise have been; this is due largely to the presence of two relatively minor gaseous constituents in the atmosphere (Section 6).

○ Name these two greenhouse gases, and state which makes the greater contribution to the greenhouse effect.

○ The two gases are carbon dioxide and water vapour. Water vapour presently makes a greater contribution to the Earth's greenhouse effect than does carbon dioxide (Section 6.5).

Why, then, is there so much concern about the amount of carbon dioxide in the atmosphere but not about the amount of water vapour? The reason is that it is difficult to see how humans can have major *direct* effects on the global water cycle — as opposed to effects that are *consequences* of other changes for which we might be responsible. However, some of our activities certainly do have direct influences on the amount of CO_2 in the atmosphere.

Activity 10.1   The effect of human activity on atmospheric CO_2

In this activity, you will revisit some of the material in Section 8, and gain more experience in writing a short account. ◀

One way to determine whether the amount of CO_2 in the atmosphere is changing at the present time is to look at one or more series of measurements taken in the recent past to see if we can detect a trend. If such a trend can be detected, then — with due caution — it can be projected through the present into at least the near future.

○ What evidence was presented in Section 8 for an upward trend in the level of CO_2 in the atmosphere during recent decades?

○ Figure 8.9 shows an overall increase in the amount of CO_2 in the atmosphere at Niwot Ridge, Colorado, from the late 1960s to the early 1990s. Figure 8.10 shows an increase over the last 250 years, based on the analysis of air trapped in Antarctic ice, and an increase since 1957 in the atmosphere at Mauna Loa, Hawaii.

○ What caused the very obvious oscillations in the levels of CO_2 plotted in Figure 8.9?

○ The oscillations were caused by seasonal variations in the rates of photosynthesis and other biological processes.

The clear superimposition of these subtle seasonal oscillations on the apparent upward trend of increasing amounts of CO_2 in the atmosphere is important. It shows that the overall upward trend cannot just be dismissed as a random fluctuation of no particular significance. Natural processes cannot account for such a large increase over such a short time period. Therefore, the increase in the amount of CO_2 in the atmosphere can reasonably be *assumed* to relate to human activities — mainly burning fossil fuel, but also forest clearance.

Since we know that CO_2 is a potent greenhouse gas, and know that its amount in the atmosphere is increasing, the GMST should also be rising. As in the case of CO_2 amounts, we can look for evidence that the GMST has risen in the recent past and then — with due caution — project any trend through the present into the near future.

Question 10.1   What two *general* methods have been used to estimate the GMST since the start of the present interglacial period? What are the main advantage and the main limitation of each method? ◀

○ By how much is the GMST believed to have risen over the past 100 years or so?

○ The GMST is believed to have risen by about 0.7 °C over the past 100 years (Figure 2.13).

Because there has been a measurable rise in the GMST in the recent past, it is probably reasonable to assume that it is still rising and that it will continue to do so for the time being. An alternative to such a modest projection of a well-established

Figure 10.1 (a) Predicted emission rates of CO_2 (expressed as $10^{12}\,kg\,C\,y^{-1}$) and (b) the corresponding predicted proportions (in p.p.m.) of CO_2 in the atmosphere, under the 'business as usual' (BaU) scenario and an alternative scenario to 2100.

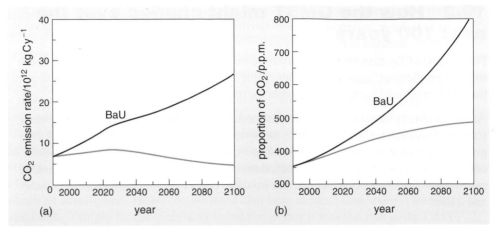

How do the rates of CO_2 emission predicted for 2000 and for 2100 compare in the BaU scenario?

From Figure 10.1a, the rate would rise from about $8.5 \times 10^{12}\,kg\,C\,y^{-1}$ in 2000 to about $26 \times 10^{12}\,kg\,C\,y^{-1}$ in 2100. Thus the rate of emission predicted for 2100 is about three times that predicted for 2000.

How do the proportions of CO_2 in the atmosphere predicted for 2000 and for 2100 compare in the BaU scenario?

From Figure 10.1b, the proportions would rise from about 370 p.p.m. in 2000 to over 800 p.p.m. in 2100. Thus the proportion predicted for atmospheric CO_2 for 2100 is more than twice that predicted for 2000.

The alternative scenario represented in Figure 10.1 is one of the more optimistic of several that have been proposed.

Question 10.3 What would happen between 2000 and 2100 to (a) the rates of CO_2 emission and (b) the proportions of CO_2 in the atmosphere under the alternative scenario in Figure 10.1? ◄

So Question 10.3 shows that, even under one of the more optimistic of the proposed alternative scenarios,

> there is likely to be a greater proportion of CO_2 in the atmosphere in 2100 than there is now; if we fail to take any action to reduce emissions (the BaU scenario), the proportion of CO_2 will more than double by 2100.

Is this the worst that can happen? Unfortunately, possibly not. As part of the carbon cycle, dissolved carbon is stored in slow-moving deep ocean currents and then released back into the atmosphere when these currents reach the surface in equatorial regions hundreds of years after 'taking the plunge' near the poles. Some scientists suspect that large amounts of industrially generated CO_2 may have become temporarily 'locked up' in these currents.

What would be the implications for future amounts of CO_2 in the atmosphere if this were so?

If we were able to get emissions of CO_2 from burning fossil fuels, etc. under control quite soon, the amount in the atmosphere should start to stabilize and might eventually start to fall sometime beyond 2100. However, we might then find that CO_2 emitted in the past comes back in the future to 'haunt' us. In other words, the Earth may already have been 'committed' to increasing amounts of atmospheric CO_2 far into the future.

Although it's easy to see that a steady state for CO_2 in the atmosphere cannot be achieved until emissions of CO_2 at least level off, it now seems that there might well be a time lag of several hundred years before the steady state is achieved even if emissions are brought under control.

Let's move on now to consider what effect increased amounts of CO_2 in the atmosphere might have on the GMST. As we do so, it's essential to bear in mind that there are complicated feedback mechanisms involved. Under certain conditions, positive feedback can lead to so-called 'runaway' effects in which a higher (or lower) GMST creates the conditions necessary for further increases (or decreases) in the GMST until a vastly different new steady state becomes established.

The effects of positive and negative feedback, as well as other complications such as coupling between factors that determine the GMST (as you have seen in 'Global warming and cooling'), means that it's very difficult to predict the consequences for the Earth's GMST of even precisely specified changes in the amount of CO_2 in the atmosphere. And, of course, we're unable to specify the size of these changes with much precision. In fact, the Earth's climate system is so complicated that the only way in which reasonably reliable predictions can be made as to how it might respond to (say) more CO_2 in the atmosphere is through the use of climate modelling, as you saw in Section 9. The Earth's climate system is therefore modelled using some of the most powerful computers available. Even so, gross simplifications have to be made, either because the phenomena modelled are insufficiently well understood in the first place or to enable the models to run fast enough to be useful. Hence, predictions made using climate models cannot, yet, be considered wholly reliable.

Activity 10.2   Summarizing climate models

In this activity, you will summarize the main achievements and limitations of climate models. ◀

Using rather more elaborate climate models than those made available to you in 'Global warming and cooling', scientists are able to carry out 'experiments' to see what the effect would be of *doubling* the amount of CO_2 in the atmosphere (a change which is likely by 2100 under the BaU scenario).

Predictions based on a doubling of atmospheric CO_2 suggest that the GMST will rise by between 1.0 °C and 3.5 °C over the next century.

We'll look at the possible consequences of such a rise in Section 10.3, but first let's try to set it in some sort of context.

Although there is still considerable uncertainty surrounding the end of the last glacial period, it is believed that the overall rise in the GMST over some 10 000 years has been about 6 °C. Almost all of this rise was in the first 1 000 years.

◯ Can you see a flaw in this argument?

◯ Just as in the case of wild organisms, crops have temperature optima and grow less well at significantly lower or higher temperatures than this.

Thus, although higher temperatures might allow more UK farmers to grow maize grain, fewer might be able to grow wheat economically. That word 'economically' is very important. Even when a crop can be grown at a particular mean temperature, it might not be economic to do so in competition with climatically more favoured areas (which is why, even if mean temperatures were to rise, the English wine industry would be unlikely to rival its French counterpart for some while).

It's also important to appreciate that the GMST is hardly likely to change independently of other aspects of climate (particularly precipitation), which are bound to influence both wild organisms and agriculture, and to have other effects as well.

A higher GMST would almost certainly lead to significant changes in the water cycle. For instance, the overall rates of both evaporation and precipitation would probably increase. It is, however, most unlikely that any increase in rainfall would be distributed uniformly (any more than rainfall itself is evenly distributed at present). Indeed, some areas may receive less rainfall than they do today and possibly suffer the effects of increased rates of evaporation into the bargain. In any case, more important than either precipitation or evaporation rates alone is the net effect of changes in the water cycle on soil moisture. Many regions will therefore be unlikely to be able to take agricultural advantage of higher average temperatures. Unfortunately, present climate models are not sufficiently sophisticated to produce reliable predictions as to which regions are likely to experience increased and which decreased precipitation.

10.3.3   Other possible effects

Another widely predicted effect of a higher GMST, and thence higher rates of energy transfer between the Earth's atmosphere and surface (whether ocean or land), is that the climate might become more 'extreme'. For example, more frequent and widespread hurricanes would inevitably cause considerable damage and disruption.

Possibly the most dramatic consequence predicted as an indirect effect of a rise in the GMST is that there would be a global rise in sea-level (Section 1).

◯ What would be the cause(s) of this rise?

◯ There would be two causes — melting of ice on land and thermal expansion of seawater.

At present it's thought unlikely that the huge Antarctic ice-sheet will melt (though changes in it are apparent). However, both mountain glaciers and the Greenland ice-sheet are likely to get smaller and so contribute to the rise in sea-level. Ice floating on the Arctic Ocean and in the sea around Antarctica would *not* make any contribution to the rise in sea-level were it to melt (if you want to prove this for yourself, try floating ice cubes in a tumbler brimful of water to see if it overflows as they melt). As seawater becomes warmer, it expands and so occupies a greater volume (Section 1). Perhaps rather surprisingly, it has been calculated that such thermal expansion of seawater will have a greater effect on future sea-levels than will the melting of glaciers and ice-sheets.

Of course, if sea-level were to rise, the sea would 'invade' the land. Low-lying areas would become vulnerable to flooding and could even 'drown' completely. There is nothing new in this. Neither the English Channel nor the Irish Sea existed in their present form until the sea-level rose after the last glacial period came to an end. As evidence of this, tree stumps that are thousands of years old are now regularly exposed at low tide at several places around the British Isles. A major difference today is that, world-wide, much low-lying land is occupied by humans. Countries such as Bangladesh would inevitably be greatly affected by even quite a modest rise in sea-level, and some Pacific and Indian Ocean island states might disappear altogether. Even the UK is far from being immune to potential rises in sea-level (Figure 1.2).

We must not overlook an important practical consequence of changes in the distributions of many organisms as a result of global warming. As far as we humans are concerned many other species are pests and some cause disease. For example, a rise in the GMST of a few degrees Celsius could help malaria to spread. Finally, recall from Section 1 that we noted that there would be consequences for transport, house heating, air conditioning, and the like.

It should be apparent that changes in the GMST of the magnitudes — and, more particularly, at the rates — predicted are bound to have significant effects on human society. As scientists, we can offer no particularly profound insights into either the precise nature of these effects or how society could or should try to cope with them. Scientists should, however, provide the best possible scientific information to inform the debate.

Activity 10.3   *Human consequences of a rise in the GMST*

This activity is intended to give you practice at planning a longer piece of writing than hitherto in this course. ◀

10.4   The Earth's climate beyond the year 2100

Notwithstanding how foolhardy such an enterprise might seem to be, some scientists have made predictions about the Earth's climate far beyond the year 2100! We thought it would be interesting to end Section 10 by summarizing some of these predictions. Of course, members of the S103 Course Team won't be around to be held accountable for the predictions described here. Rather more dramatically, because very few species manage to survive for more than a few million years, it's quite likely that there will be *no* members of our species around to check on the longer-term predictions — although we might have given rise to one or more descendent species before our species' own demise. Although you might find these ideas somewhat disturbing initially, they do at least have the merit of encouraging us to focus on planet Earth and its various life-forms in a less human-centred way than usual.

It's generally accepted that our best guide to the Earth's climate in the distant future is our knowledge of its climate in the past, and quite a lot is known about climates in the distant past (Sections 3 and 9).

Much beyond the next few thousand years, the Earth's climate is more likely to be influenced by natural events than by the sorts of human-induced change we have concentrated on so far in Section 10. Some of these events are rather unpredictable in detail, such as temporary increases in volcanic activity causing more solar radiation to be reflected back into space by dust and aerosols in the atmosphere. Others are more regular and hence predictable, for example changes in the Earth's axial tilt and in its orbit around the Sun.

Based on our understanding of the past pattern of ice ages and glacial/interglacial periods, it's thought likely that the Earth will experience a cold period about 5 000 years from now and an even colder one after about 22 000 years, *if there were no human enhancement of the Earth's greenhouse effect*. Then, in about 50 000 years time, the next glacial period would get underway. Although we're not certain by how much humans are enhancing the Earth's natural greenhouse effect at present — or how much CO_2 might eventually be returned to the atmosphere from the deep oceans — it seems extremely unlikely that *any* action on our part could delay the start of the next glacial period much beyond about 65 000 years from now.

The Earth is then expected to follow a pattern of alternating glacial and interglacial periods for about 65 Ma, perhaps punctuated by the effects of one or more impacts by major comets or asteroids. Such impacts were common during the very early history of the Earth and one probably contributed to the demise of the dinosaurs 65 Ma ago. Immediately after any such impact the Earth would cool down considerably, owing to the reflection of solar radiation back into space from the huge amounts of dust that would be thrown up into the atmosphere. These dust clouds would also inhibit photosynthesis for a year or more after an impact.

As briefly mentioned in Section 9.2.2, and as you will learn in Block 3, the Earth's continents have not always been distributed as they are today. So-called 'continental drift' is known to have had a strong influence on the Earth's climate in the past. For instance, the Gulf Stream came into existence about 3 Ma ago when North and South America joined together, and has since kept western Europe warmer than it otherwise would have been. Also very significant for the climate is whether a large landmass is present at the South Pole on which vast amounts of ice can accumulate. Over a time-scale of 65–600 Ma, the continents are thought likely to move towards the Equator and possibly coalesce there to form a 'supercontinent', as they did about 225 Ma ago when a supercontinent known as Pangaea existed. In these circumstances, there would be little scope for the formation of polar ice-caps and much of the Earth might become *very* hot and wet.

On the very longest view into the future, after a few billion years, the Sun's luminosity will increase considerably as the Sun ages. Unless much of this radiation is reflected back into space, the Earth will become *much* hotter and only rather different forms of life would be able to survive on its surface. Ultimately, the planet will be sterilized by a runaway temperature increase, as follows. The rise in the GMST would greatly increase the rate of evaporation of water, and the higher temperature of the atmosphere would enable it to hold more water vapour. Moreover, the increase in the temperature of the surface ocean would mean it could hold less dissolved carbon (Section 8.4.4). There would thus be more water vapour and more CO_2 in the atmosphere, and the consequent increased greenhouse effect would drive the temperature up further. Stabilizing influences that might come into play while the increase in the solar luminosity was only modest would be overwhelmed by a large increase in the solar luminosity of the ageing Sun.

If this long-term view is correct, the Earth would end up with all its water in the atmosphere. More of its carbon would also be released into the atmosphere as the high temperatures caused carbonate rocks to decompose. The consequence would be a **runaway greenhouse effect**, causing the GMST to be many hundreds of degrees Celsius. It is possible that the planet Venus, being closer to the Sun than is the Earth, experienced such a runaway greenhouse effect in its distant past: this is certainly one way of accounting for its present GMST of 460 °C, and the huge amount of CO_2 in its atmosphere.

Thus, when the solar luminosity starts to rise considerably, no life will be be able to exist on Earth.

10.5 Summary of Section 10

The amount of CO_2 in the atmosphere has increased since at least the start of the industrial revolution. The GMST has risen for the past several hundred years. Though a correlation between two phenomena does not prove that one causes the other, climate models indicate that the increased amount of CO_2 in the atmosphere has probably caused at least some of the rise in the GMST.

Under even the most optimistic of the scenarios used to predict future CO_2 emissions, the amount of CO_2 in the atmosphere will increase until at least 2100.

Dissolved carbon stored in slow-moving deep ocean currents may be released into the atmosphere as CO_2 in hundreds of years time.

The current best estimate from climate models is that the GMST will rise by between 1.0 and 3.5 °C by 2100.

Some species will probably adapt to life at these temperatures; some will migrate so as to continue living in similar temperatures; and others will become extinct, thereby reducing the Earth's biodiversity.

A higher GMST will:

- have major effects on agriculture;
- be accompanied by other climate changes, such as increased rates of precipitation and evaporation;
- result in the melting of ice-caps and the thermal expansion of seawater, with a consequent rise in sea-levels;
- possibly lead to more problems with pests and diseases;
- affect transport, and the need for heating and air conditioning of dwellings, work places, etc.

As a result of climate change, there is likely to be social disruption even in those countries and regions that might otherwise be regarded as 'winners'; the effects on people living in low-lying areas, and in regions that may become drier, are likely to be profound.

Irrespective of any possible human enhancement of the greenhouse effect, the Earth's climate will undergo major changes in the longer term leading, in a few billion years, to the planet's sterilization as the Sun's luminosity increases as it ages.

Activity 2.1 Measuring precipitation (continued)

Before finishing Block 2, you should complete the analysis of your results for this practical work, and determine a mean value for daily precipitation. ◀

11 Summary and forward link

This is a very brief summary of Block 2. For a more detailed overview you should read the section summaries.

In this block we have introduced a wide range of scientific ideas, and applied them in a quest to understand what determines the Earth's surface temperature. There can be no doubt that a rise or fall of a few degrees has significant effects on life on Earth, human and otherwise. For most of the block the surface temperature has been represented by a single value, the global mean surface temperature, or GMST.

The GMST depends on the ways in which the Earth's surface gains energy, and the ways in which it loses energy. In the steady state, the rate of gain equals the rate of loss. If the gain exceeds the loss then the GMST rises until a new steady state is reached at a higher value. Conversely, if the energy loss exceeds the gain, then the surface cools to a new steady state value of the GMST. Of particular importance in determining the GMST are the solar constant, and various properties of the Earth's surface and atmosphere.

Greenhouse gases in the atmosphere raise the GMST, and the two greenhouse gases that are of particular importance are water vapour and carbon dioxide. The amounts of these gases in the atmosphere are determined by complex global cycles.

There is plenty of evidence for temperature changes in the distant past, and particular attention was paid to fossils and to land-forms, including those produced by glaciation. For the most recent past there is an instrumental record, and this shows a clear increase in the GMST over the past 100 years or so.

In order to understand past changes in the GMST, a variety of climate models can be used. At present our understanding is significantly limited by our lack of knowledge about important processes that operate in the Earth's complex climate system, such as cloud formation. For all but the most recent past there is also lack of knowledge about factors that determine climate, such as the solar constant. Additionally, for the distant past, there is lack of knowledge about the global climates themselves. Consequently, the further we go into the past the less reliable are the calculations of the climate models. For the recent past, the best models indicate that the biggest single cause of the rise in GMST over the past 100 years or so is an enhanced greenhouse effect, caused by CO_2 (and other gases) released into the atmosphere by human activities.

Many models also attempt to explain other aspects of climate, such as precipitation, and they also try to account for regional climates. In both endeavours they are less successful than in their attempts to explain changes in the GMST.

The models that are used to understand past changes in climate are also used to predict future changes. The predictions for the climate over the next 100 years or so depend on human activities from now on, particularly on the release of CO_2 and other substances into the atmosphere. A range of possibilities has been considered, and there is general agreement that, by 2100, the GMST will probably be between 1.0 °C and 3.5 °C higher than it is today.

Though this block is complete in itself, it points forward to the rest of the course. In exploring the fascinating problem of the Earth's surface temperature, the scope of science has, to some extent, been revealed. Science sets itself the task of uncovering the behaviour of the natural world, and of trying to explain this behaviour. It has had considerable success with this endeavour, but, as exemplified by the study of the Earth's surface temperature, there is still much that we do not know, or do not understand.

You are now ready to explore the world of science itself, rather than a particular problem that science has tackled. Science tends to divide into traditional areas each with a characteristic 'flavour'. The four main areas are biology, chemistry, Earth science and physics, and in each of Blocks 3–11 there is an emphasis on one of them. However, the study of the Earth's surface temperature has drawn on a wide range of topics from all four areas, illustrating that the boundaries between them are not distinct. To some extent we shall indicate the distinguishing features of the four main areas of science as we go along, but we shall also be concerned to establish links between them. Many of the interesting problems in science now involve more than one traditional area.

One mode of exploration of the world of science is to find out what things are made of, and to explain their behaviour in terms of the component parts. This is a journey that, broadly speaking, is from the large to the small, and it is a journey that we shall make in Blocks 3–7 of the course. We start in Block 3 with the largest possible structure, no less than the whole Universe, though we shall quickly home in on the Earth, and discover the place of our planet in the scheme of things.

Activity 11.1 Reviewing your study of Block 2

Block 2 has introduced you to a lot of new science, as well as developing new skills. In this concluding activity, you will review how well you have achieved the block objectives and how you have adapted your study methods to deal with the variety of topics discussed. ◀

Questions: answers and comments

Comments on the answers are given in curly brackets {...}.

Question 1.1 {A huge variety of examples can be given, so there are very many satisfactory responses to this question. If your answer included one from each of the following lists then that's fine. If you included examples that are not listed here then they might well be appropriate, though you should re-examine such cases to make sure they are sensitive to an average temperature change of a few degrees Celsius.}

All of the following are likely to change:

The natural environment: types of tree, bird, insect, and wild animal; sea-level; snow cover.

Agriculture: types of crop, farm animal, or pest that damage crops.

Housing: heating bills; air conditioning bills; house design.

Transport: the need for snow-clearing equipment; the number of accidents involving ice or snow; snow and ice closure of airports, railways and sea ports.

Question 2.1 The maximum temperature is 25.2 °C and was reached at 18.00 hours, or 6 o'clock in the afternoon. The minimum temperature is 15.0 °C and was reached at 03.00 hours or 3 o'clock in the morning. {Reading information from graphs is discussed in Box 3.3 of Block 1, and in *SGSG* Maths Help 10.}

Question 2.2 (a) 0.43 m + 1.217 m = 1.647 m, or 1.65 m to two decimal places. {Note that when adding and subtracting, you have to think of *decimal places* rather than significant figures; the number of decimal places in the answer is the same as the smallest number of decimal places in the calculation.}

(b) 8.1 kg − 3.82 kg = 4.28 kg, or 4.3 kg to one decimal place.

(c) 2.373 m × 3.6 m = 8.542 8 m², or 8.5 m² to two significant figures. {Note that when multiplying and dividing, the number of *significant figures* in the answer is the same as the smallest number of significant figures in the calculation.}

(d) 6 342 kg/2.42 m³ = 2 620.661 2 kg m⁻³, or 2.62 × 10³ kg m⁻³ to three significant figures.

Question 2.3 (a) The number of temperature values is twice the number of days, i.e. 2 × 365. Thus, from

Equation 2.2:

$$\text{annual mean surface temperature} = \frac{6\,647\,°C}{2 \times 365} = 9.1\,°C$$

{Note that we have expressed the answer to two significant figures, as requested. Though the sum of the temperatures obtained by adding together the 2 × 365 individual measurements is given to four significant figures, we quote the mean to only two significant figures because the thermometer reading is likely to be accurate to only ±0.1 °C. The sum 6 647 °C is not given to the first decimal place because it has involved the addition of many numbers.}

(b) To obtain a more accurate value, the temperature would have to be measured at regular times more often than twice a day. {For example, in the case of the data from Milton Keynes in Table 2.1, the mean of the readings taken at 06.00 hours and at 18.00 hours is 20.5 °C, whereas the mean of the 24 hourly readings is 19.0 °C. The latter is clearly a more accurate summary of the temperatures recorded throughout the 24 hour period. This is because frequent regular measurements reduce a systematic uncertainty that arises neither from the instrument (the thermometer) nor its environment, but from the times at which measurements are taken.}

Question 2.4 (a) The sum of the mean surface temperatures is 87.3 °C, and there are nine surface locations. Therefore, from Equation 2.2:

$$\text{UK 30-year mean surface temperature} = \frac{87.3\,°C}{9} = 9.7\,°C$$

{Again we have limited the answer to two significant figures, as requested, rather than the three in the sum of the temperatures, because the thermometer scales are unlikely to be accurate to better than ±0.1 °C.}

(b) A more representative value would be obtained if there were more locations, uniformly spread over the UK.

Question 2.5 (a) The curves have similar shapes, and the maximum temperatures are the same. {In detail, they show that pronounced cooling started shortly before 18.00, and warming started at about 06.00. These times will of course vary between seasons and be different for different locations on the Earth, as will the exact temperatures reached.}

(b) The main difference between the curves is that the lowest night-time temperature reached at the urban site is greater than that reached at the rural site. {This is a consequence of the lower cooling rate in the evening at the urban site.}

Question 2.6 The data in Table 2.3 indicate that, with increasing population, the urban heat island intensity will increase. The urban mean temperature depends on this intensity, and also on the surrounding rural mean temperature (Figure 2.9). The urban mean temperature will increase provided that the surrounding rural mean temperatures do not fall too much. {Note from Figure 2.9 that the urban heat island intensity is mainly caused by higher night-time temperatures. Therefore, if the intensity increases, this implies increased urban night-time temperatures.}

Question 3.1 There are 365 days in a year, 24 hours in a day, 60 minutes in an hour and 60 seconds in a minute. Therefore

$$1 \text{ year} = 365 \text{ days} = 365 \times 24 \text{ hours}$$

$$= 365 \times 24 \times 60 \text{ minutes}$$

$$= 365 \times 24 \times 60 \times 60 \text{ seconds}$$

$$= 31\,536\,000 \text{ seconds} = 3.153\,6 \times 10^7 \text{ seconds}$$

Thus

$$0.3 \text{ metre per year} = \frac{0.3}{3.1536 \times 10^7} \text{ metre per second}$$

$$= 9.51\ldots \times 10^{-9} \text{ metre per second}$$

and

$$600 \text{ metres per year} = \frac{600}{3.1536 \times 10^7} \text{ metre per second}$$

$$= 1.90\ldots \times 10^{-5} \text{ metre per second}$$

The correct abbreviation for metres per second is $m\,s^{-1}$. The speed 0.3 metre per year is given to just one significant figure, and so we assume that 600 metres per year is also given to one significant figure, so the answers should be given to one significant figure. Thus, $9.51\ldots \times 10^{-9}$ rounds up to 10×10^{-9}, or 1×10^{-8}, and $1.90\ldots \times 10^{-5}$ rounds up to 2×10^{-5}. So the answer is that typical speeds of glaciers may vary between $1 \times 10^{-8}\,m\,s^{-1}$ and $2 \times 10^{-5}\,m\,s^{-1}$.

Question 3.2 V-shaped valleys are a sign that glaciation has not occurred whereas U-shaped valleys are evidence for glaciation. Temperatures decrease as altitude

increases, therefore we would not expect to find unglaciated regions at higher altitudes than glaciated regions. {Of course, the reverse is possible and is observed at many places.}

Question 3.3 Figure 3.10 includes grains of pollen from Scots pine (the large grain at the right centre of Figure 3.10) and oak (the grain looking like a tennis ball on the lower edge of the picture). {Also visible are grains of hazel pollen (above the Scots pine grain and left of centre), heather pollen (the dark grains to the right of the pine grain) and a fern spore (the semicircular grain on the upper right edge). Note that a complete reconstruction of the plant population requires the identification and counting of hundreds of pollen grains from a single sample, not just the few grains that appear in Figure 3.10.}

Question 3.4 (a) Somewhat more than 80% of the tree pollen in the interval between 6.5 and 7.5 m is birch pollen.

(b) In the upper half of the core, birch accounts for about 10 to 15%, although values of between virtually zero to a little more than 20% are present.

(c) The old parts of the core are buried by younger layers of material. The percentage of birch pollen has therefore decreased in going from old (deep) to young (shallow) samples.

Question 3.5 Trees require average summer temperatures greater than about 10 °C, so the times when tree pollen is most poorly represented are expected to have been the coldest. These lie below about 18 m and between about 4.5 and 12 m depth in Figure 3.14.

Question 3.6 {According to Figure 3.15, there were short periods when the mean temperature was changing fairly rapidly (e.g. about 10 000 years ago), and at other times (e.g. around 100 000 years ago) the estimated mean temperature fluctuated considerably. In these cases it can be tricky to read values from the graph accurately, but you should have found answers close to those given below.}

(a) About 9 to 11 °C {similar to, or a little warmer than, today's mean annual temperature}.

(b) About 2 to 7 °C {some 2.5 to 7.5 °C colder than today's mean annual temperature}.

(c) About 2 to 6 °C {some 3.5 to 7.5 °C colder than today's mean annual temperature}.

(d) About 3 to 9 °C {up to about 6 °C colder than today's mean annual temperature, although temperatures at slightly older and younger times were a few degrees warmer, but barely reached today's value}.

Question 3.7 The pollen fossils allow us to estimate temperature values at particular sites, and the layer-by-layer record provides a detailed sequence of temperature values through time, which are tied to dated ages. In contrast, evidence from glacial landscapes indicates widespread (regional) cold conditions, but the exact temperatures involved, any fluctuations in temperature and the ages involved cannot be discovered from this approach alone.

Question 3.8 (a) 1 Ga = 10^9 years, so 2.1 Ga = 2.1×10^9 years.

(b) 1 Ma = 10^6 years, so 570 Ma = 570×10^6 years = 5.7×10^8 years, to two significant figures.

(c) 1 ka = 10^3 years, so 140 ka = 140×10^3 years = 1.4×10^5 years. {The use of prefixes with units is discussed in Box 3.1 of Block 1, and in *SGSG* Chapter 5, Section 4.2.}

Question 3.9 (a) 19 500 years can be written as 19.5×10^3 years, to three significant figures; since 10^3 years are 1 ka, 19 500 years can thus be written as 19.5 ka.

(b) 115 000 years can be written as 115×10^3 years and 0.115×10^6 years, or 115 ka and 0.115 Ma, respectively.

Question 4.1 (a) For a given amount of water (2 litres), if the temperature rise is smaller (10 °C compared with 80 °C), then less energy is required.

(b) For a given temperature rise (80 °C), if the amount of water is smaller (1 litre compared with 2 litres), then less energy is required.

Question 4.2 From Equation 4.1,

$$\text{power} = \frac{\text{energy transferred}}{\text{time taken}}$$
$$= \frac{6.7 \times 10^5 \, \text{J}}{335 \, \text{s}} = \frac{670\,000 \, \text{J}}{335 \, \text{s}} = 2\,000 \, \text{J s}^{-1} = 2\,000 \, \text{W}$$

{This is 2 kW. Note that to do this sum on your calculator you should have keyed in 6 . 7 EE 5 ÷ 3 3 5 =; see Block 1, Box 6.1.}

Question 5.1 (a) With the bulb in a steady state, the bulb must be gaining energy at the same rate that it is losing it, i.e. 60 W. This power comes from the electric current flowing through the bulb. {Any reference to electrical power, the mains, etc. will suffice as an answer to where the energy comes from.}

(b) If the Sun is also in a steady state {and it is}, it must have an internal power source equal to the power that it is radiating. {This source is nuclear power in the Sun's core.}

Question 5.2 (a) The greater the proportion of visible solar radiation that a region reflects or scatters, the brighter the visual appearance of the region.

(b) The bright material at A is cloud over the equatorial region, whereas that at B is Antarctic ice and snow. {'Cloud' is an acceptable answer for B — it is not easy to tell cloud from ice and snow in the polar regions in Figure 5.6}. The dark material at C is water — the Atlantic Ocean, seen through a break in the clouds.

Question 5.3 The fractions of intercepted solar energy are as follows, followed by the decimal forms, and then by the percentages.

(a) $\dfrac{\text{scattered and reflected}}{\text{intercepted}} = \dfrac{31\,\text{units}}{100\,\text{units}} = \dfrac{31}{100} = 0.31$

which as a percentage is $0.31 \times 100\% = 31\%$.

(b) $\dfrac{\text{absorbed by atmosphere}}{\text{intercepted}} = \dfrac{20\,\text{units}}{100\,\text{units}} = \dfrac{20}{100} = 0.20$

which as a percentage is $0.20 \times 100\% = 20\%$.

(c) $\dfrac{\text{absorbed by surface}}{\text{intercepted}} = \dfrac{49\,\text{units}}{100\,\text{units}} = \dfrac{49}{100} = 0.49$

which as a percentage is $0.49 \times 100\% = 49\%$.

{If you need more practice with fractions, decimals and percentages, then you should study the 'Practising maths skills' software on the Block 1 CD-ROM or *SGSG* Maths Help, Sections 3–5.}

Question 5.4 Convection involves upward motion of air in the atmosphere. Pollutants released at ground level will thus be carried upwards and diluted, and so they will not concentrate near the ground.

Question 5.5 If there is no convection and no wind, then the layer of air next to the ground is not removed. If the water vapour in this layer is not carried away then the further evaporation of water from the surface is inhibited. Therefore, the only latent heat extracted from the ground is for the initial evaporation.

Question 5.6 Figure 5.12 shows that, the higher the GMST, the greater rate at which the Earth's surface emits radiation. This supports the assertion that, as the GMST rises, the rate of energy loss from the Earth's surface increases.

Question 5.7 (a) (i) For the Earth as a whole, the total rate of energy gain (solar radiation intercepted) is 100 units, and the total rate of loss is the sum of the upward pointing arrows at the top of the atmosphere. This is 31 units + 57 units + 12 units, i.e. 100 units — a difference of zero.

(ii) The total rate of energy gain by the Earth's surface is the sum of the downward pointing arrows that penetrate the Earth's surface in Figure 5.14. This is 49 units + 95 units, i.e. 144 units. The total rate of loss is the sum of the upward pointing arrows that originate at the Earth's surface: 30 units + 114 units, i.e. 144 units. The difference is again zero.

(iii) Proceeding as in (ii), the total rate of energy gain by the atmosphere is 20 units + 30 units + 102 units, i.e. 152 units, and the total rate of loss is 95 units + 57 units, i.e. 152 units. Again the difference is zero.

(b) From (ii), at the Earth's surface the rate of gain of energy equals the rate of loss. The surface is therefore in a steady state and so the GMST is not changing. {Likewise, from (iii), the mean atmospheric temperatures will not be changing. From (i), the Earth as a whole is in a steady state.}

Question 6.1 As you saw in the video 'The particle model', there is nothing between the gas particles except empty space — a vacuum (Section 5.1).

Question 6.2 (a) Since sample A is at a higher temperature than sample B, the particles of sample A are, on average, moving faster than the particles of sample B.

(b) As you saw in the video 'The particle model', the particles of a gas are continually bumping into each other and exchanging energy. Thus when we mix the two samples together, the higher speed particles of sample A will collide with the lower speed particles of sample B, thus decreasing the speeds of particles of sample A, and increasing the speeds of particles of sample B. Eventually the average speeds of all the particles become the same. {Since the temperature of a gas is reflected in the speed of the particles, the final temperature will be somewhere between the initial temperatures of the two samples.}

Question 6.3 The air is just like any other substance and can exist as a gas, liquid or solid. So if we cool the air down sufficiently we would expect it first to condense to give liquid air and then if we cool it further it will freeze to give solid air. {However, as we shall see in Section 6.3, air is a mixture of different gases and so does not behave in such a straightforward manner. The different components in the air condense and freeze at different temperatures.}

Question 6.4 In (a)–(c) both numbers are raised to the same power of ten, so we can simply add the two numbers accompanying the powers of ten.

(a) $(2.3 \times 10^3) + (3.5 \times 10^3) = (2.3 + 3.5) \times 10^3$
$= 5.8 \times 10^3$

(b) $(5.6 \times 10^{-5}) + (2.9 \times 10^{-5}) = (5.6 + 2.9) \times 10^{-5}$
$= 8.5 \times 10^{-5}$

{Box 6.2 in Block 1 explains how to enter negative powers of ten on your calculator.}

(c) $(7.4 \times 10^4) - (4.3 \times 10^4) = (7.4 - 4.3) \times 10^4$
$= 3.1 \times 10^4$

(d) This differs from (a)–(c) only in that we have to apply the rule for subtracting a negative quantity, i.e. it is the same as adding the quantity.

$(7.4 \times 10^4) - (-4.3 \times 10^4) = (7.4 - (-4.3)) \times 10^4$
$= (7.4 + 4.3) \times 10^4 = 11.7 \times 10^4 = 1.17 \times 10^5$

(e) Here the powers of ten are different, so we need to convert the numbers into a form with a common power. We choose the smaller (10^3), so we can rewrite the question as:

$(65.6 \times 10^3) + (3.3 \times 10^3) = (65.6 + 3.3) \times 10^3$
$= 68.9 \times 10^3 = 6.89 \times 10^4.$

{You could equally well rewrite the question as:

$(6.56 \times 10^4) + (0.33 \times 10^4) = (6.56 + 0.33) \times 10^4$
$= 6.89 \times 10^4$}

(f) We choose 10^4 as the common power, so we can rewrite the question as:

$(753 \times 10^4) - (3 \times 10^4) = (753 - 3) \times 10^4$
$= 750 \times 10^4 = 7.50 \times 10^6$

(g) Here the powers of ten are not only different but one is positive and the other negative. However, again we simply choose the lower power of ten as the common power, and so 3.754×10^2 is written as $3\,754 \times 10^{-1}$. Thus, we can rewrite the question as:

$(3\,754 \times 10^{-1}) - (3 \times 10^{-1}) = (3\,754 - 3) \times 10^{-1}$
$= 3\,751 \times 10^{-1} = 3.751 \times 10^2$

{More help with calculations involving powers can be found in *SGSG* Maths Help, Section 7.}

Question 6.5 (a) First we multiply the two numbers accompanying the powers of ten:

$$(2.5 \times 10^7) \times (4.0 \times 10^2) = (2.5 \times 4.0) \times (10^7 \times 10^2)$$
$$= 10 \times (10^7 \times 10^2)$$

Adding the two powers of ten:

$$10 \times (10^7 \times 10^2) = 10 \times 10^{(7+2)} = 10 \times 10^9$$
$$= 1.0 \times 10^{10}$$

(b) We follow the same procedure as for (a):

$$(4.2 \times 10^8) \times (3.0 \times 10^{-5}) = (4.2 \times 3.0) \times (10^8 \times 10^{-5})$$
$$= 12.6 \times 10^{(8-5)} = 12.6 \times 10^3 = 1.26 \times 10^4$$

(c) Again the procedure is as for (a) and (b):

$$(3.2 \times 10^{-4}) \times (3.0 \times 10^{-3}) = (3.2 \times 3.0) \times$$
$$(10^{-4} \times 10^{-3}) = 9.6 \times 10^{(-4 + (-3))} = 9.6 \times 10^{-7}$$

(d) First we divide the two numbers accompanying the powers of ten, that is 3.6 divided by 1.8, which gives us 2.0:

$$\frac{3.6 \times 10^6}{1.8 \times 10^2} = \left(\frac{3.6}{1.8}\right) \times \left(\frac{10^6}{10^2}\right) = 2.0 \times \left(\frac{10^6}{10^2}\right)$$

Subtracting the two powers of ten:

$$2.0 \times \left(\frac{10^6}{10^2}\right) = 2.0 \times 10^{(6-2)} = 2.0 \times 10^4$$

{We express the answer to two significant figures, because the numbers that we are dividing are both given to that precision.}

(e) $\dfrac{2.4 \times 10^5}{6.0 \times 10^2} = \left(\dfrac{2.4}{6.0}\right) \times \left(\dfrac{10^5}{10^2}\right) = 0.40 \times \left(\dfrac{10^5}{10^2}\right)$

$$0.40 \times \left(\frac{10^5}{10^2}\right) = 0.40 \times 10^{(5-2)} = 0.40 \times 10^3 = 4.0 \times 10^2$$

(f) $\dfrac{2.5 \times 10^3}{5.0 \times 10^7} = \left(\dfrac{2.5}{5.0}\right) \times \left(\dfrac{10^3}{10^7}\right) = 0.50 \times \left(\dfrac{10^3}{10^7}\right)$

$$0.50 \times \left(\frac{10^3}{10^7}\right) = 0.50 \times 10^{(3-7)} = 0.50 \times 10^{-4} = 5.0 \times 10^{-5}$$

(g) $\dfrac{2.5 \times 10^3}{5.0 \times 10^{-7}} = \left(\dfrac{2.5}{5.0}\right) \times \left(\dfrac{10^3}{10^{-7}}\right) = 0.5 \times \left(\dfrac{10^3}{10^{-7}}\right)$

$$0.50 \times \left(\frac{10^3}{10^{-7}}\right) = 0.50 \times 10^{(3-(-7))} = 0.50 \times 10^{10} = 5.0 \times 10^9$$

{More help with calculations involving powers can be found in *SGSG*, Maths Help, Section 7.}

Question 6.6 (a) Reading from Table 6.1, there are 5.2×10^{20} particles in a cubic metre at 80 km and 2.6×10^{25} particles in a cubic metre at sea-level. To work out the percentage we divide the value at 80 km by the value at sea-level, and multiply the result by 100%, that is:

$$\frac{(5.2 \times 10^{20})}{(2.6 \times 10^{25})} \times 100\%$$

We can rewrite this as:

$$\left(\frac{5.2}{2.6}\right) \times \left(\frac{10^{20} \times 10^2}{10^{25}}\right)\% = 2.0 \times 10^{(20 + 2 - 25)}\%$$
$$= 2.0 \times 10^{-3}\%$$

(b) We calculate the pressure at 80 km (1.3×10^{-5} bar) as a percentage of that at sea-level (1.0 bar) in a similar fashion:

$$\frac{(1.3 \times 10^{-5}\,\text{bar})}{1.0\,\text{bar}} \times 100\%$$

We can rewrite this as:

$$\left(\frac{1.3}{1.0}\right) \times 10^{-5} \times 10^2\% = 1.3 \times 10^{(-5 + 2)}\% = 1.3 \times 10^{-3}\%$$

(c) Table 6.1 shows that both the number of particles in a cubic metre and the pressure decrease with increasing altitude.

{Although the calculations above show that the number of particles per cubic metre, and the pressure, decrease by roughly the same amount between sea-level and 80 km — to about 1 or $2 \times 10^{-3}\%$ of sea-level values — they do not decrease to *exactly* the same percentage.}

Question 6.7 The higher the plane flies, the lower the density of the air. In terms of our particle model, as the plane flies it has to push the air particles out of the way and this is the cause of the air resistance. There are fewer particles per unit volume at higher altitudes than at lower altitudes (Table 6.1), so at higher altitudes there is less air to push out of the way and so the plane can go faster for the same energy input.

Question 6.8 Figure 6.18 shows the change of state. Particles of water in the solid state are arranged in specific positions. When a water particle sublimes it moves from the solid into the gaseous state, where it is free to move. Energy needs to be supplied to overcome the attraction between the particles in the solid.

Question 6.9 There are 10 blue particles and 10 red particles, so the total number of particles is 20. In terms of the number of particles, the percentage of each type is

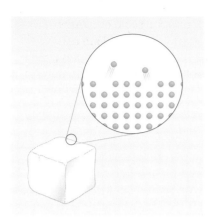

Figure 6.18 The transition of a solid directly into a gas — the process of sublimation.

$\frac{10}{20} \times 100\% = 50\%$, that is 50% blue particles and 50% red particles. The total mass of blue particles is 10×10 g, that is 100 g. The total mass of red particles is 10×1 g, that is 10 g. The total mass of all particles is 100 g $+ 10$ g, that is 110 g. In terms of the mass of particles, the percentage of blue particles is $\left(\frac{100 \text{ g}}{110 \text{ g}}\right) \times 100\% = 91\%$, that is 91% blue particles, and the percentage of red particles is $\left(\frac{10 \text{ g}}{110 \text{ g}}\right) \times 100\% = 9\%$, that is 9% red particles. {A useful check is that the percentages add up to 100%. Indeed, $91\% + 9\% = 100\%$.} Clearly, the percentage is different depending on whether we calculate it on the basis of mass or on the basis of the number of particles. {We meet the same problem when we bake a cake. For a particular ratio of ingredients we will get a different result depending on whether we measure the ingredients by mass or by volume! Thus it is important to identify on which basis the calculation is performed, or the data are presented, since without this information the figures are meaningless.}

Question 6.10   Sample (a) contains two types of molecule: hydrogen molecules with two hydrogen atoms bonded together and oxygen molecules with two oxygen atoms bonded together. This is a mixture.

Sample (b) contains only water molecules, which each consist of two hydrogen atoms and one oxygen atom. Since the sample contains only water molecules, it is a pure sample of water. {A mixture of hydrogen and oxygen gases behaves very differently from water — for one thing the mixture will explode if ignited! So the way in which atoms are arranged in molecules is important, not only in the way that we classify them, but also in their properties.}

Question 6.11   (a) Because a methane molecule is made up of more than one type of atom, methane is a chemical compound.

(b) Figure 6.13 shows that methane contains two types of atom: one represented by a dark grey ball, and the other represented by pale grey balls. These correspond to atoms of carbon and hydrogen, respectively.

(c) Each molecule of methane contains one carbon atom and four hydrogen atoms.

(d) There are four chemical bonds in each molecule of methane. Each bond is between a carbon atom and a hydrogen atom.

Question 6.12   The atmosphere of Venus is mainly (about 97%) CO_2. The remainder is chiefly nitrogen, with small amounts of sulfur dioxide, water, oxygen and argon.

The atmosphere of the giant planet Jupiter is predominantly (about 87%) hydrogen, most of the rest being the noble gas helium.

Question 6.13   Helium is used because it is safer. As we saw earlier, helium is a noble gas and is unreactive so there is no danger of it reacting with oxygen, as hydrogen would.

Question 6.14   The products of a chemical reaction contain the atoms that were present in the reactants. The reaction between the elements hydrogen and oxygen can produce water but not carbon dioxide, because there is no carbon in the reactants. Methane is a compound that contains both carbon and hydrogen, so when it reacts with oxygen both carbon dioxide and water are formed. {This agrees with the rule that atoms of chemical elements are neither created nor destroyed in a chemical reaction.}

Question 6.15   On Venus, the atmosphere is mainly carbon dioxide. There is a little oxygen, but not enough to allow us to breathe for very long or to light a fire.

The atmosphere of Jupiter is mainly hydrogen. Again we couldn't breathe. Although hydrogen catches fire on Earth, it would not ignite on Jupiter because there is no oxygen for it to react with. {However, we could light a fire if we took a cylinder of oxygen with us! Remember that we need both fuel and oxygen to make a fire: on Earth we are surrounded by oxygen and need a cylinder of fuel; on Jupiter we would be surrounded by fuel (hydrogen) and need a cylinder of oxygen.}

Question 6.16   Reaction 6.3 shows that petrol reacts with oxygen to give carbon dioxide and water. These exit from the engine via the exhaust. This reaction gives out energy that is used to move the car. {Many people believe that the petrol is in some way converted into energy and only a little waste material exits from the exhaust. In fact one litre of petrol (about 1 kg) reacts with about 4 kg of oxygen from the air to produce 5 kg of waste gases, that is 3.5 kg of carbon dioxide and 1.5 kg of water vapour, and these escape through the exhaust.}

Question 6.17   Like argon and the other noble gases, neon does not exist as molecules but as single atoms. It therefore does not have any bonds to absorb infrared radiation. As Figure 6.13 shows, methane exists as a molecule and contains more than two atoms, so it absorbs infrared radiation and is a greenhouse gas.

Question 6.18   The atmosphere of Venus is mainly carbon dioxide, a greenhouse gas. The atmosphere contains far more particles per cubic metre than the Earth's atmosphere, so we would expect there to be a greenhouse effect on Venus that is much larger than that on Earth. {These expectations are borne out. On Venus there is so much carbon dioxide in the atmosphere that the greenhouse effect increases the GMST by several hundred degrees Celsius.}

Question 7.1   If the mean daily precipitation measured in Activity 2.1 (in February) had fallen every day of the year, then the annual precipitation would be 365 times the mean daily value. This is unlikely to be the same as that in Figure 7.2, for two reasons. First, the month of February is unlikely to be typical of the whole year. Second, the data in Figure 7.2 are averages over several years, and there is no reason to expect the precipitation for this year to be exactly that for the average year.

Question 7.2   (a) The mean annual precipitation for each site is obtained by adding together the data for each month. For Liverpool this is 843 mm, for Cambridge it is 526 mm, and for New Delhi it is 596 mm.

(b) Liverpool is in a mid-green region on Figure 7.2 and so has a possible mean annual precipitation in the range from 800 to 1 200 mm. Cambridge is in a white region, with a mean annual precipitation in the range 0–600 mm. The values calculated in part (a) fall within these ranges.

(c) Liverpool has a mean annual precipitation similar to the global mean. Cambridge and New Delhi are considerably drier, but New Delhi is slightly wetter than Cambridge — on average!

{The shortcoming of mean annual precipitation values is that they do not reveal the seasonal variations. This is particularly apparent in New Delhi, where most of the precipitation occurs in just four months.}

Question 7.3   There is a much greater variation in the month-by-month evaporation of water during a year than in the month-by-month precipitation. The precipitation is fairly constant throughout the year, but the evaporation peaks in the summer because of the higher temperature.

Question 7.4   During the winter months precipitation is greater than evaporation and so the lakes fill up. However, during the summer months evaporation is greater than precipitation so the lakes are more prone to drying up. {This can be seen by superimposing Figures 7.3 and 7.6; see Figure 7.11.}

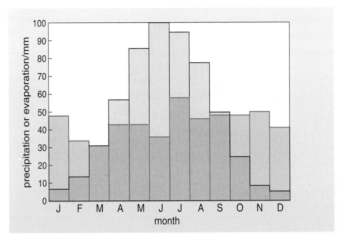

Figure 7.11   A comparison between precipitation in East Anglia and evaporation from a lake.

Question 7.5   First, the rate of evaporation or sublimation will depend on the temperature. As oceans will be warmer than snow-covered areas, we might expect evaporation from the oceans to occur more readily than sublimation from snow. Second, because the particles are held more tightly in a solid than in a liquid, sublimation requires more energy than evaporation. So again, we might expect sublimation from snow to occur less readily than evaporation from the oceans. {This is indeed the case.}

Question 7.6   If the mean annual precipitation over equivalent areas of ocean and land were the same, we would expect the precipitation in kilograms per year over the oceans to be about two and a half times as large as the precipitation over the land. In fact, the total precipitation over the ocean (398×10^{15} kg y^{-1}) is roughly four times greater than the total precipitation over the land (107×10^{15} kg y^{-1}). This indicates that the mean annual precipitation (in millimetres) over the ocean is greater than the mean annual precipitation over the land.

Question 7.7 The residence time of water in ice and snow is so much larger than that in the oceans, even though the reservoir is much smaller, because the rate at which water moves from the ice into other reservoirs is so low. From the answer to Question 7.5, once the water is frozen it will not readily flow or evaporate.

Question 8.1 From Table 8.1, the rock reservoir contains $50\,000\,000 \times 10^{12}$ kg of carbon; 1 p.p.m. is one-millionth of this, so divide by 1×10^6:

$$\frac{50\,000\,000 \times 10^{12}\,\text{kg C}}{1 \times 10^6} = \frac{50 \times 10^6 \times 10^{12}\,\text{kg C}}{1 \times 10^6}$$

$$= 50 \times 10^{12}\,\text{kg C}$$

{Note that we have retained the 10^{12} kg C unit used for all carbon reservoirs.}

The atmospheric reservoir is 760×10^{12} kg C, so the percentage increase is

$$\frac{50 \times 10^{12}\,\text{kg C}}{760 \times 10^{12}\,\text{kg C}} \times 100\% = 6.6\%$$

{Thus a tiny change in the rock reservoir makes a substantial change in the much smaller atmospheric reservoir.}

Question 8.2 The time to remove all of the CO_2 through photosynthesis is the total amount in the atmosphere divided by the amount removed each year by photosynthesis:

$$\frac{760 \times 10^{12}\,\text{kg C}}{120 \times 10^{12}\,\text{kg C y}^{-1}} = \frac{760}{120\,\text{y}^{-1}} = 6.3\,\text{y}$$

Question 8.3 One possible answer is that since the Southern Hemisphere summer occurs during the Northern Hemisphere winter, and vice versa, the pattern of CO_2 proportion should be shifted by about six months: falling at the beginning of the year (Southern Hemisphere summer), and rising in the middle of the year (Southern Hemisphere winter).

Another possible answer is that since there is less land, and therefore less seasonal growth of vegetation, in the Southern Hemisphere than in the Northern Hemisphere, the size of the seasonal change should be smaller.

{Both differences are observed.}

Question 8.4 (a) Comparison of the horizontal axes shows that Figure 8.9 extends the CO_2 record back for 25 years before 1993, whereas Figure 8.3 extends back for only 3 years before 1993. In Figure 8.9 the vertical scale covers a larger range in order to include the lower proportions of CO_2 in earlier years.

(b) The general trend is a steady increase in the amount of atmospheric CO_2 over the whole 25-year period shown.

Question 8.5 (a) Between 1700 and 1900, the rate of increase was slight but noticeable. (b) Between 1900 and 1950 the rate of increase was rather greater, as reflected in the somewhat steeper 'slope' of the graph. (c) Since 1950, the rate has continued to increase faster and faster, and the 'slope' of the graph has got steeper and steeper.

Question 9.1 The other energy gains and losses that determine the GMST are as follows.

Gains at the Earth's surface: absorption of solar radiation; absorption of infrared radiation from the Earth's atmosphere.

Losses from the Earth's surface: evaporation of water (latent heat); emission of infrared radiation.

Gains by the atmosphere: absorption of infrared radiation from the Earth's surface; heat convected from the Earth's surface; condensation of water (latent heat).

Losses by the atmosphere: emission of infrared radiation.

{Any four of these constitute the required answer. Note that reflection and scattering of radiation are not included; these are not really gains or losses.}

Question 9.2 If the fraction of the Earth covered in ice and snow increases then the planetary albedo increases, and so a greater fraction of solar radiation is reflected away. The GMST therefore falls. This causes a further increase in the fraction of the Earth covered in ice and snow, and hence a further increase in the global surface albedo, and a further reduction in the GMST. We thus have a fall in GMST causing a further fall in the GMST, which is positive feedback. {This will not go on for ever, even if the GMST stabilizes only when the whole Earth is covered in ice and snow!}

Question 10.1 For the past few hundred years, air temperatures have been measured directly using thermometers (Section 2). Such data are presumably related quite directly to the GMST — although allowance does have to be made, particularly in the early records, for possible bias in the siting of thermometers (e.g. predominantly in or near towns, especially where there is urban expansion).

Information about glaciers and fossil organisms has also been used to estimate past temperatures (Section 3). This method is less direct than the use of thermometers, necessitating even more careful interpretation of the measurements. However, it doesn't rely on individuals having kept weather records at particular times and places in the past, nor does it suffer from many of the biases of these written records — although it may well introduce biases of its own. And, of course, it allows the record to be extended much further back into the past.

Question 10.2 {The question asks you to give the answer as a list. One way of doing this is in the form of a 'bulleted' list, as follows.}

Further factors that affect the GMST are:

*   the value of the solar constant {probably the most obvious factor};

*   the value of the Earth's planetary albedo {the proportion of solar radiation reflected straight back into space, for instance by clouds, aerosols, or the Earth's surface};

*   those that relate to energy losses from the Earth's surface, i.e. convection, latent heat and infrared radiation;

*   those that relate to the absorption and emission of radiation by the atmosphere, i.e. aerosols and the proportions of greenhouse gases (other than CO_2) in the atmosphere.

Question 10.3 (a) From Figure 10.1a, the rate of CO_2 emission would fall from about 8.5×10^{12} kg C y^{-1} in 2000 to about 5×10^{12} kg C y^{-1} in 2100. Thus the rate of emission predicted for 2100 would be about two-thirds of that predicted for 2000.

(b) From Figure 10.1b, the proportion of CO_2 in the atmosphere would rise from about 370 p.p.m. in 2000 to about 490 p.p.m. in 2100. Thus the proportion predicted for 2100 would be more than 30% greater than that predicted for 2000.

Question 10.4 (a) A rise of 6 °C in 1 000 years is equivalent to $\frac{6\,°C}{1000\,y} = 0.006$ °C y^{-1}. Therefore, the rise in a decade would be 0.006 °C $y^{-1} \times 10\,y = 0.06$ °C per decade.

(b) Taking the predicted rise in the GMST over the next century as 2.5 °C (about the middle of the range of predictions given in the text, i.e. 1.0–3.5 °C), gives a rate of 0.25 °C per decade.

These calculations suggest that the Earth is presently warming about four times faster than at the end of the last glacial period.

Question 10.5 Temperature records for the two geographical areas would support the claim if they showed different mean temperatures. But even if they did, how could we be sure that the distributions are determined by the mean temperatures? For instance, more significant than the mean temperature might be either the minimum or the maximum temperature, or perhaps another aspect of climate (e.g. rainfall). Alternatively, the presence or absence of certain other animal or plant species may be far more important than any aspect of climate.

{A possible explanation of the British distributions of the two species is that the ground vole is gradually being displaced by the rather larger water vole. The absence of both sorts of vole from Ireland might be the result of a failure to re-colonize Ireland after the last glacial period before it was cut off from Britain by the return of the Irish Sea. Thus, we have to be aware that the present distribution of a species might have as much to do with its history as its preferences for different climatic conditions.}

Question 10.6 It could mean that the species formerly spent the entire year in a particular area, but then adapted so that it moved south for the winter and returned north for the following summer (seasonal migration). On the other hand, it could mean that the species' distribution became more southerly (permanent migration).

In the case of seasonal migration, the change could have been brought about by individual animals developing the habit during their lifetimes. Alternatively, it could be the result of the differential survival or reproduction of animals with a genetic tendency to migrate seasonally, or of the survival of those who were better at migration.

In the case of permanent migration, there could have been a general tendency for individual animals to move south during the course of their lifetimes, or it could be that animals at the southern end of the distribution tended to survive to adulthood or reproduce more successfully than those at the northern end.

Acknowledgements

Grateful acknowledgement is made to the following sources for permission to reproduce material in this block:

Figures

Figure 1.2: United Kingdom Climate Change Impacts Review Group for the Department of the Environment, *The Potential Effects of Climate Change in the United Kingdom*, January 1991, © Crown Copyright. Reproduced with the permission of the Controller of Her Majesty's Stationery Office; F*igure 2.1*: © Crown Copyright. Reproduced with the permission of the Controller of Her Majesty's Stationery Office; *Figure 2.7*: Courtesy of the University of Oxford, School of Geography; *Figure 2.8*: Jones, P. D. and Bradley, R. S. 1992, 'Climatic variations in the longest instrumental records', *Climate Since A.D. 1500*, Routledge; *Figures 2.10 and 2.12*: Parker, D. E. *et al.* 1992, 'A new daily Central England temperature series, 1772–1991', *International Journal of Climatology*, **12**, Royal Meteorological Society; *Figure 2.13*: Parker, D. E. *et al.* 1996, 'Global and regional climate in 1995', *Weather*, **51**(6), Royal Meteorological Society; *Figures 3.3 and 3.5*: Courtesy of Tony Waltham; *Figure 3.4*: Landform Slides; *Figure 3.6a*: the British Geological Survey copyright © NERC, all rights reserved; *Figure 3.7*: John, B. S. 1977, *The Ice Age*, HarperCollins Publishers Ltd; *Figure 3.8a*: Natural History Museum; *Figure 3.8b*: courtesy of R. A. Spicer; *Figure 3.10:* courtesy of C. Turner; *Figure 3.11*: courtesy of C. J. Hawksworth; *Figures 3.12 and 3.13*: West, R. G. 1977, *Pleistocene Geology and Biology*, 2nd edition, p. 362, reprinted by permission of Addison Wesley Longman Ltd; *Figure 3.14*: Reprinted with permission from *Nature*, **281**, 18 October 1979, p. 559, Woillard, G. 1979, 'Abrupt end of the last interglacial S. S. in North-East France', copyright © 1979 Macmillan Magazines Limited; *Figure 3.15*: Reprinted with permission from *Nature*, **338**, 23 March 1989, p. 312, Guiot, J., Pons, A., de Beaulieu, J. L. and Reille, M. 1989, 'A 140,000-year continental climate reconstruction from two European pollen records', copyright © 1989 Macmillan Magazines Limited; *Figure 3.16*: Brown, G. C., Hawkesworth, C. J. and Wilson, R. C. L. 1992, *Understanding the Earth*, 2nd edition, Cambridge University Press; *Figure 5.6*: NASA; *Figure 6.8*: IBM Corporation, Research Division, Almaden Research Center; *Figure 7.2*: Meteorological Office 1978, *Map of Average Annual Rainfall 1941–1970*, © 1978 Crown Copyright. Reproduced with the permission of the Controller of Her Majesty's Stationery Office; F*igures 7.6 and 7.11*: *Water Resources: Planning for the Future*, Anglian Water Authority; *Figures 8.3 and 8.9*: Conway, T. J., Tans, P. P. and Waterman, L. S. 1994, 'Atmospheric CO_2 records from sites in the NOAA/CMDL air sampling network', pp. 41–119, in Boden, T. A., Kaiser, D. P., Sepanski, R. J. and Stoss, F. W. (eds) *Trends '93: A Compendium of Data on Global Change*, September 1994, ORNL/CDIAC-65, Carbon Dioxide Information Analysis Center, Oak Ridge National Laboratory, Oak Ridge, Tennessee, USA; *Figure 8.4*: Norman T. Nicholl, Aberdeen; *Figure 8.5a*: Andrew McIntyre, Lamont-Docherty Geological Observatory, Columbia University; *Figure 8.5b*: Dee Breger, Lamont-Docherty Geological Observatory, Columbia University; *Figure 8.8*: courtesy of A. S. Payne; *Figure 8.10*: Houghton, J. T., Jenkins, G. J. and Ephraums, J. J. (eds) 1990, *Climate Change: The IPCC Scientific Assessment*, Cambridge University Press, copyright © Intergovernmental Panel on Climate Change 1990; *Figure 10.1*: Houghton, J. T. *et al.* (eds) 1996, *Climate Change 1995: The science of climate change*, copyright © Intergovernmental Panel on Climate Change 1996; *Figure 10.2*: van den Brink, F. H. 1967, *Field Guide to the Mammals of Britain and Europe*, HarperCollins Publishers Ltd.

Photo on title page

Geoscience Features Picture Library.

Index

Entries and page numbers in **bold type** refer to key words which are printed in **bold** in the text and which are defined in the Glossary. These are terms that we expect you to be able to explain the meaning of, and use correctly, both during and at the end of the course. An entry followed by ^{G} indicates a term which is defined in the Glossary but which is not bold in the text. Where the page number is given in *italics*, the indexed information is carried mainly or wholly in an illustration or table. Section summaries and answers to questions are not indexed.

S103 Course Team

S103 *Discovering Science* was produced for the Science Faculty by a team drawn from many areas of the Open University. The full list of contributors to the course is printed in the S103 *Course Guide*.

Block 2 was produced for the S103 Course Team by the team of people listed below.

Block Chair:	Barrie Jones (Physics)
Authors:	Stephen Blake (Earth Sciences), Nancy Dise (Earth Sciences), Barrie Jones (Physics), Pat Murphy (Biology), Peter Taylor (Chemistry)
Course Team Chair:	Stuart Freake
Course Manager:	Isla McTaggart
Editor:	Dick Sharp
OU Graphic Design:	Sarah Crompton, Ruth Drage, Alison George, Pam Owen, Howard Taylor
Centre for Educational Software:	Philip Butcher, Chris Denham, Ian Every, Rufus Wondre
BBC/OUPC:	Marie Jefsioutine, Paul Manners, Gloria Medina (Science Faculty), Liz Sugden, Nicholas Watson
External course assessor:	Prof. Paul Black (King's College, London)
External block assessor:	Dr Keith Shine (University of Reading)

The block has also benefited greatly from comments and other forms of help during its production from Chris Ashley (Associate Lecturer, AL), Audrey Brown (AL), David Campbell (AL), Sally Jordan (AL), Clive Lawless (Institute of Educational Technology), Judith Metcalfe, Len Newton (AL), Tony Pallot (AL), Annie Payne, Kiki Warr, Helen Wood (AL) and all the students who tested materials.